The Child From Nowhere

The Child
From Nowhere

FREDA
LIGHTFOOT

CANELO

First published in the United Kingdom in 2004 by Hodder & Stoughton Ltd.

This edition published in the United Kingdom in 2019 by

Canelo Digital Publishing Limited
57 Shepherds Lane
Beaconsfield, Bucks HP9 2DU
United Kingdom

A CIP catalogue record for this book is available from the British Library.

Print ISBN 978 1 78863 395 6
Ebook ISBN 978 1 78863 259 1

Look for more great books at www.canelo.co

Printed and bound in Great Britain by Clays Ltd, Elcograf S.p.A.

Chapter One

High in the Langdales where the sun was striking the pikes over Dungeon Ghyll, slanting silvered rays across to Hardknott Pass, a young boy, small for one very nearly six years of age, was carrying buckets of water from a nearby beck up to the farmhouse door where he poured it into a large boiler. He kept spilling it and soaking his legs and feet because he was in a hurry, knowing that if it wasn't filled by the time the farmer's wife came downstairs, he'd get a beating from her husband. He might get one anyway, simply for being there, for existing, although there were times when the boy felt he must be invisible, since it was rare for the farmer to even speak to him, and never by name.

'Hey you,' he would say. 'Fetch t'milk in. Look sharp.'

And young Alan would rush to carry out this order to the letter, fearful of what might befall him if he didn't. He'd come not to expect praise or gratitude for the work he did. He knew that however hard he laboured, he was considered to be of no account on this farm, because he was of less use than the sheep and hens who produced meat and eggs, and the family cow who gave them rich, creamy milk. In comparison with the other children, who were the farmer's own, he was seen as a second-class citizen.

Sometimes he dreamed of what it must be like to have a mother. There were times when he could see her in his mind's eye. She had glorious red coloured hair, rather like his own only brighter, and it fell in soft tendrils about her neck and shoulders. Her eyes were a clear grey and her skin soft and pale as silk. He loved that face, nursed it in his heart whenever he was weeping with cold and loneliness, when the bruises stung too much.

Later, when the boiler was filled, he would have to turn the handle on the mangle, pitting his scrawny muscles and sticklike limbs against the weight of the rollers. Unlike the farmer's own children Alan didn't go to school, but stayed all day on the farm to help with the chores: chopping thistles, picking stones, mending walls and endlessly filling water troughs and fetching feed for the sheep. Alan never went anywhere, save occasionally to market with the farmer, and then only to fetch and carry, or to be used along with the sheep dogs to guard and shepherd the sheep. Sometimes he'd go into Keswick or Ambleside with Mrs Brocklebank, the big fat farmer's wife, to help her carry the butter and eggs she had to sell, or mind the stall. He loved these outings, as they were the only bright moments in what was otherwise a dull and lonely life.

He was certainly never allowed to eat in the big, warm kitchen, but took his meals in the cold, draughty barn which was also where he slept, among the cobwebs, which he really didn't mind as the spiders were his friends. He would talk to them for hours, telling them of things which might have been memories, or then again only dreams. Sometimes, if there were ewes brought in after lambing, he'd creep down very quietly and sleep beside them where it was all warm and cosy. They never seemed to mind, and even a sheep as a mother was better than none at all.

–

'I've decided what I'm going to do,' Kate announced to Millie one day. It was some weeks after the birth of her child, the baby girl who was the result of a guilty indiscretion with Eliot Tyson, her erstwhile employer, and the man she loved. Not that she'd give him the satisfaction of letting him know that fact. He'd demanded to know if the child was his and she'd refused to tell, insulted that he could think so little of her when they'd been through so much together. Hadn't she trusted him with her own son's life, allowed him to adopt the boy when she'd found herself with no other way to feed him? At least she'd been allowed to stay on as Callum's nursemaid, if not as his mother. Amelia, Eliot's late wife and unable to have children herself, had taken on that role. Kate remembered her sweet mistress with great affection.

Which added to her shame of having lain with her husband, albeit if it hadn't been until after the good lady's sad death.

And here in her arms was the result of that union. Kate had named the child Flora because she looked as sweet and precious as a flower, hoping with all her heart that this new life would help her to carry on. She would never forget the child she had lost, her lovely Callum who had disappeared one bright autumn afternoon, never to be seen again. But at least now she had a reason to go on living. And one day, if she kept looking hard enough, she believed she would eventually find him. She had to believe that, if she was not to fall into that dark pit again.

The soreness of a difficult birth was easing, even the bleeding was starting to dry up and Kate was feeling well enough now to think about the future. In her hand was an envelope addressed to her. It had come days ago but she hadn't yet plucked up the courage to open it although she recognised the handwriting. She knew it was from Eliot, could feel the bulk of a key inside and guessed it was for the cottage he'd promised her.

In these last few weeks while she'd been recovering from having Flora, she'd made up her mind to accept his offer, for the baby's sake. Much as she now hated him for all he'd done, not least for taking Callum from her in the first place and now accusing her of being some sort of whore who slept around, she knew Eliot was right when he said the

4

pair of them couldn't stay here, in Poor House Lane. Without Kirkland Workhouse at the end of the yard to protect them, it was more dangerous and soul-destroying than ever. They'd be better off living on the open fells, which she could always do if it came to that, Kate thought with a show of her old defiance. Except that she'd made other plans. 'I have everything all worked out, to be sure.'

Millie looked up from her work with interest, glad to hear a brighter note in her friend's voice. 'You've decided to tell him he's the father then, have you?'

'I have not! If he can so easily think me capable of lying with another man so soon after being with him, he doesn't deserve to be given a second chance.' Kate settled the baby in the Moses basket and came over to sit by Millie, watching the stubby, stained fingers work the needle and thread in and out of the leather sole of the shoe she was making. 'No, no, I'm going to beat him at his own game. Since Eliot refuses to listen to a word I say against Swainson, that despicable little swine of a man who thinks he can control us just because we're women and poor, then I'll find another way to fight him. Fight them both, so I will, if it takes me last breath.'

Millie stopped her sewing to listen, jaw slack as she took in the vehemence of her friend's anger, panic rising in her breast. 'Fight him in what way? What are you saying, Kate? And what's Swainson got to do with your future? Nay, don't you do owt you might regret, summat we might all regret.'

'Indeed, I wouldn't regret a thing, I do assure you.'

'Just remember that I depend upon the work I get from that swine of a man as you call him, to feed me childer. Don't ever forget that.'

'I don't forget it, and I don't like it any more than you do. So pin back yer lug-holes and listen.' She leaned closer, dropping her voice as if the filthy walls themselves had ears, or the vermin that scratched within them could comprehend her plan. 'I was thinking that Eliot Tyson was right, that we should get out of this stinking pit.'

'Oh aye, and pigs might fly.'

Kate chuckled and held up the key, reading the note which went with it to Millie. It urged her to accept the cottage, if not for her own sake, then for the child's. 'If he weren't such an arrogant, opinion-ated bastard, wouldn't I still be in love with him?'

'You still are in love with him.'

'I am not!' She held up a hand as Millie would have pressed the matter further. 'Are you going to listen to me, or what? I was thinking of that money he so kindly put into a bank account for me. Not that I know much about how banks work, but I dare say they'll explain how I can get me hands on it. I didn't want to touch it at first because I was soft in the head over him, still suffering from that girlish crush I had.'

'Girlish crush my aunt Fanny, it were more n' that. Didn't you love the bones of him?'

'Are ye going to listen to what I have to say, or sit there and keep interrupting?'

'All right, go on. I'm listening.'

'I was thinking that all these women who work for Swainson could just as easily work for me, that there are men too in these yards who'd be glad of a bit extra and have the skills at their fingertips.'

'Help you with what? How can *you* find 'em work? You don't have any orders for shoes! Have you lost yer mind, Kate O'Connor?'

Kate chuckled. 'Mebbe I have but I never felt better in me life, so help me. If Eliot Tyson can get orders for shoes, so can I, with a good workforce to back me up, particularly if we undercut him on price. I swear I could do better than Tyson's lot any day of the week.'

'And what about Callum?'

Kate took a few moments to answer this, needing to get that undertow of emotion under control, as always, before she could speak normally about her son. 'Oh, I'll find him one day, so I will. He's somewhere around. I just have to find out where. In the meantime, I have another child to feed, and life must go on, for her sake. In case you haven't noticed, Millie, there's a war coming, and what is it folk need on their feet in wartime? What did they need in the Crimea?'

Millie looked blank. 'There won't be no war. That's just talk. Anyroad, folk don't wear shoes in wartime, Kate. They wear boots.'

Kate beamed. 'Exactly! So all I have to do is get an order from the army to make boots, then rent a room in which to make them, and we're away, so we are.'

'And what do you know about making boots?'

'Not much, but I can learn. I can find someone who'll teach me what's needed. Mebbe I could get our Dermot to come back from Ireland and help.'

'It won't happen,' Millie insisted, scoffing at the very idea. 'Even if you did succeed in making a load of boots, there won't be no war, and then where would you be? With a load of stuff you couldn't even sell.'

'The important thing is not *if* war will start, but that we're ready for it when it does. In the meantime, we make boots. Lots of them. I learned that much from Eliot Tyson. Get a warehouse and put stock in it, and once shopkeepers know you have goods ready and waiting, they'll buy it. We won't be going in for fancy shoes, nor them posh Napoleons or whatever they call them hunting, shooting and riding boots Tyson's make for gentlemen. We'll make good, solid, working men's boots. We can make 'em for farmers or factory hands as well as soldiers, for anyone who needs the dratted things. I'll use the money Eliot Tyson gave me to buy whatever machinery we need, get meself some men, and women, to operate them, and set up in competition to him. It'd be worth it just to save the women from that nasty piece of shite.'

Millie's mouth was gaping open in shock. 'You're serious, aren't you? You've thought this all out.'

'To be sure, I'm serious. I've been thinking on this for weeks while I've been laid up here. If Eliot Tyson can steal my son off me, neglect and lose him, take advantage of me and then accuse me of sleeping with another chap when I've just given birth to his daughter, his first and only child, mind, he deserves everything I can throw at him. He deserves for me to steal his business in return.'

'Ooh, Kate, ye've lost yer senses.'

'No Millie, I've just found them. Eliot Tyson is about to learn that Kate O'Connor is not the sort of woman who takes ill-treatment lightly, not on me own account, nor for the women in his employ. We'll put him out of business, see if we don't.'

–

Getting started was the hardest part. Kate's first problem was to persuade people to trust her. Everyone thought her quite mad. She went round the neighbouring yards seeking workers, but many bluntly told her she'd lost her mind and slammed the door in her face. Others politely declined on the grounds they daren't take the risk. Women such as Sally Wilshaw, Joan Enderby and Nell Benson told her that anyone would be mad to give up secure employment to go and work for her; untried, unsafe and ignorant as she was.

It was made clear that despite their distress and unhappiness over the current situation, the women were fearful of change. Children still had to be fed, and if Kate's new business didn't survive, Swainson might not take them back. Then where would they be?

'What will I do if no one will work for me, Millie?' Kate complained, night after night. 'I never thought of that. Why won't they trust me?'

'Because they're scared. Give them time. They'll come round.'

Undeterred, she rented an old abandoned rope works which would provide the space she needed, and give ready access to the railway. It took all of her nerve to approach the landlord but, despite the scathing disbelief in his face, he was willing enough to draw up a three-year lease in return for six months' rent in advance.

'You'll have gone bump by then,' he scorned, clearly thinking he could let his property all over again to some other fool.

'Oh no, I mean this business to thrive and prosper.'

She wrote to Dermot, hoping he might come back from Ireland to help her, and spoke to one or two of the old chaps who sat about doing nothing all day because they'd been 'turned out to grass' as they put it, by Swainson. When she suggested they might like to put their skills back in use again, they looked doubtful.

'D'you mean work for thee? How can a li'le lass like you offer us a job?

'Why not?' Her heart beat fast with the temerity of her cheek, and wasn't in the least surprised when the old men burst out laughing.

Kate shrugged her thin shoulders. 'It's up to you. You can believe in me or not, as you choose, but what have you got to lose? At worst you get a few months' paid work. At best, you get steady employ-ment for years to come.'

They considered her with greater thoughtful-ness, knowing she'd had a bairn recently, and yet had been a widow this many a long year. They'd heard the gossip, listened to their wives sniffing their disapproval and tearing her to shreds. But there was something about the lass, no one could deny it. A certain audacity in the way she tilted her chin and met their scepticism with a steady gaze, challenging them to dispute the feasibility of her scheme, if they dare. With her arms folded, shoulders back and spine rigid with purpose, no one could doubt her deter-mination to succeed. She'd stand on her own two feet, this one, and not beg for pity. So they agreed to give the plan a try. As she rightly said, what did they have to lose?

These men proved more than able to help her find second-hand Blake sewing machines, wooden and iron lasts, and the right finishing machinery needed for her to make a start. And old Gabriel, who'd taught her brother his trade, stood at her elbow when she went to buy the leather, pointing out the flaws, the marks and small holes made by the blowfly, all of which damaged the quality of the finished product. All she needed now was to get the women on her side, the very ones she'd wanted to help in the first place.

The first to come round was Sally Wilshaw from the next yard. She came late one night, sporting a black eye and bruised ribs. 'That devil has beaten me once too often. *And* he's refused to pay me wages, all because I told him he couldn't have any how's-yer-father this week, because I weren't feeling so bright. Nasty beggar clocked me one, then punched me in t'stomach, right in front of t'childer.'

'You mean Swainson?'

'Course I mean Swainson. Who else?'

'Have you not thought to complain to Eliot Tyson about what he does to you?'

Sally's face filled with a mixture of fear and scorn. 'When have the toffs ever listened to the likes of us? Swainson is the one wi' the power, because he's the one what hands out the work, week after week. You knows that as well as I do, lass. So think on, when you get up and running, let me know. I, for one, will be willing to give you a try. I surely can't be any worse off.'

'Tell him to sling his hook, you're working fer me now,' Kate said, eyes bright with hope. This was the breakthrough she'd dreamed of, for one of the women to give her a chance. 'Here's yer first week's wages,' she said, slipping several shillings into the astonished woman's hand. 'Be at the old ropeworks first thing tomorrow. I'll find ye summat to do, even if it's only sweeping the floor.'

'Hey, watch that generosity of yours,' Millie warned her, as the woman scuttled off. 'You will be going bump if you throw yer money around so freely.'

'You have to invest in folk, in order to win them over. And what about you, Millie? Will you be giving me a try, or are you sticking with Swainson?'

There was a long drawn-out pause while Millie cast her eye over her sleeping children. Clem was at the Cock and Dolphin, as usual. Even when he wasn't, he rarely brought home more than a shilling or two. Nothing had improved in all of these long weary years, in fact quite the opposite. There were more and more children to be fed, eleven the last time she'd bothered to count. And who had stood by her all this time? Who had provided clothes for their backs, food for their empty bellies? She looked at her friend and gave a rueful smile. 'How can I refuse? But I want one o' them top jobs, soon as yer mekking a bit o' brass.'

Kate hugged her tight. 'You and me stick together, right?'

–

Word got around and Sally proved to be the first of many. Once they realised that there was an alternative to Swainson's bullying, when they saw how hard Kate was prepared to work herself, how determined she was, they were soon queuing up for jobs.

They flocked to the workshop she'd opened in the old ropeworks, knocked on her cottage door at all hours of the day and night till, in the end, Kate was turning folk away, although promising to keep a note of their name, just in case. She paid better wages than Tyson's, offered shorter working hours and no outwork, no dust and filth going into people's homes. None of this business of two hours' work before breakfast, therefore no children forced into labour too, no blind eye turned when they 'helped mam out'.

'And best of all,' Millie reminded them, 'no Swainson coming to leer and poke his filthy fingers, or his cock, where he shouldn't, using and abusing us women whenever it takes his fancy.'

'You can count me in,' they said, one after the other.

'This is going to work,' Kate said, hugging her friend with glee.

'So all you have to do now, is sell the boots we make, otherwise we'll have the flipping things coming out of us ears.'

Chapter Two

Even the sound of the name, the Great War, brought a chill to Kate's heart. How could there be anything great about a war in which thousands of people would die? She supposed it meant that millions more would be saved, that men would be fighting for 'Honour, Justice, Truth and Right', or so it said every day in the newspapers. But how many mothers' sons would need to die before that was achieved? Not hers. She no longer had a son, although today, October 10, 1914, he would be eleven years old. Too young to fight, thank God. Wherever he might be, he would at least be spared that.

Not for a moment, let alone a day, had the memory of Callum slipped from her mind in all of this time. He was forever there, a part of her soul, living and breathing inside her head. And she had never given up hope of finding him. Without that, she might truly have gone mad. Somewhere, Kate was certain, Callum was alive and well, just waiting for her to bring him home.

'Where are ye, me cushla? Mammy loves you,' she would whisper, a dozen times a day.

There were times when she'd wonder what on earth she was doing working herself into a state of exhaustion when she should be out looking for her son. Days when she would find herself falling into a reverie, staring into the stark reality that she had no family, no one to call her own with her brother off somewhere in Ireland. She'd had only one letter from Dermot, and that begging for money. She'd sent it, of course. Rapscallion or not, he was her only kin.

But if she ever thought she was wasting her time, she'd think of Millie and all the other women she'd saved from Swainson's unwelcome attentions, wipe away the tears of self-pity and get back to work. There was nothing more to be done about Callum, but she was at least doing something useful with her life.

And she did have a daughter. Kate counted her blessings every day for that fact, hardly able to bear being separated from little Flora. Even now she still sometimes woke with that sinking feeling in her stomach, that familiar sensation of loss rushing in upon her like a great black tide. Her first instinct was always to reach for Flora as the child was never far from her side, not for a moment.

Kate glanced across at her now, where she was playing with her doll on the clippy rug. A pretty little thing with dark brown wavy hair, like her father, that had a sufficient hint of red in it to mark her Irish background, together with his chestnut-brown eyes and Kate's own pale complexion. A beauty in the making with her pert little chin, snub nose and sparkling personality. Very much the little madam, and quite able to twist anyone who came within smiling distance around her smallest finger.

The last five years had not been unkind, had proved surprisingly profitable in fact. Perverse to a fault, she had returned the key to Eliot and declined his offer of a cottage, determined to do things her own way. But she'd held on to the money, viewing it as a loan, making the decision that he owed her that much at least, for all the pain and loss she'd suffered.

It had been hard at the beginning, taking much more effort than she'd anticipated to get going properly. The money Eliot had given her hadn't been anywhere near enough but the bank had been willing enough to lend her what she needed later, once they were satisfied that money was flowing and some profit being made. In addition to the women and the old men who first came to work for her, Kate had soon found a few younger men ready to make a bit extra on top of the wages they already earned at Tyson's by doing a bit of part-time work in the evenings.

And so, with everything in place and boots being made, she'd gone out on the road two days a week, taking her box of samples with her, and if at first shopkeepers had given her quizzical looks and been reticent to trust in her because she was a woman; had appeared sceptical when she promised to deliver the very next day should they require it, Kate hadn't allowed their negative attitude to deter her.

'I'm selling these fine strong boots at sixteen shillings and ninepence a pair, twopence less than you'd pay at Tyson's. It's an opening offer to encourage you to give us a try and if you buy more than twenty-five pairs, I'll give you a five per cent discount. Like I say, assuming we have all the sizes you want, ye can have them delivered tomorrow, first thing.'

'And will you give me ten per cent if I buy fifty?' asked one astute customer.

Kate swallowed, swiftly decided to take a chance and agreed that she could. She'd worry about her costing later. What she needed right now was cash flow, or so the bank manager had carefully explained to her.

In the end her charm and winning smile won through. Few could deny her at least the opportunity to prove herself. Within eighteen months, she was seeking more men willing to work for her, needing them to be full-time. And then she secured an order for two hundred pairs of boots from a customer supplying several large engineering firms in Birmingham, with the promise of more later.

She'd gone back to Kendal in a lather of excitement and worry. 'Do we have two hundred pairs? Can we deliver them?'

They did, and they could, sending the goods by rail. It was the first of many such orders and Kate had known, in that moment, that the future of her business was secure.

Today, Kate had twenty clickers working for her. These were the men who cut the leather, and in the closing room she had near on a hundred women and girls putting it all together to form the uppers. The soles were cut by thirty or so men in another room using machines designed specially for the purpose. In the final part of the process, the machinist eased the boot onto the last, bringing the welt and boot together. Last of all, the boot was burnished and buffered and polished, paired off and strung together. After that they were sent to the packing room, where they were marked, sized up, and packed ready for dispatch.

She'd acquired the much hoped for order from the army, and her own workshop, small by comparison, was way ahead of Tyson's in providing boots for the forces. She'd succeeded to such an extent that recently she'd been approached by the Russians, to supply them too. Kate fully intended to open a whole new department for them alone soon.

Once having got the business going, Kate and Flora, together with Millie, Clem and the children, had moved into one of the better yards off Highgate, renting a white-washed limestone cottage which had three bedrooms, in addition to the kitchen and a privy all to themselves. Luxury indeed. Here, with her friends, she'd found a sort of peace, if not exactly happiness. That was a state she could never entirely achieve, not without Callum. Happiness would have to wait until the day she found him, although she still hoped to attain contentment someday, were she ever able to fill that other void in her life, the lack of a good man's love. There were several around who would have been more than willing to fit the bill.

In this yard alone there was Josh the cabinet maker who'd begged her to wed him, as he was in need of a wife to mind his three children. Then there was William the printer, a shy man who had sent her a very formal letter listing his not inconsiderable assets. There was Mervyn, who worked at the tannery down by the river, not forgetting Thomas Hodgson, who'd taken quite a shine to her and offered to share his large corner property and thriving metal workshop with her.

'You're a bonny lass, and I'd do me best to mek thee happy,' he would say. 'How can you resist my ample charms? Aren't I handsome enough for you?'

'Course you're handsome, Tommy. I really don't know how I resist you, but I fear I must try. I'm far too busy to even think of marriage right now. Sorry, love.'

Just as well she did. Tommy was one of the first to join up, attending the Territorial Army training camp in July 1914, leaving for France only a few weeks later.

'I'm that excited,' he told her. 'I've never been further than Blackpool afore. You will write, won't you lass?'

She wrote every week, gently ignoring his oft repeated, and increasingly ardent proposals. But he never did see even one Christmas on foreign soil, as he was returned to his elderly mother in a coffin before the year was out.

Kate was sad but didn't regret her decision. She was content to remain single and devote all her energies to her business. She'd wanted only one man and he had let her down, supposedly because he was way above her station, or didn't trust in her morals. Whatever the reason, he'd never properly understood her. The reality, in Kate's mind at least, was that he had failed her at a much more intimate level. Now, five years on from their last meeting, she saw herself very much as his equal. She'd made something of herself, achieved a great deal, and if initially it had been with the money he gave her, the main part of her success had been down to her own efforts. Her stubborn determination not to be beaten by life.

Further contingents of optimistic young men continued to leave from Kendal station, new boots highly polished, and with hope and patriotism burning high in their hearts. Many, like Kate's devoted suitor, did not return. Some were drowned when their ships were sunk, others died of festering wounds, or returned home having lost their sight, or a limb. Some were more fortunate and came home to Kendal to be treated for their injuries at the VAD. hospital that was set up in the Friends' Day School, before being sent back to the front, into the 'jaws of hell', for more punishment. By the spring of 1915 over a thousand young men had joined the Kendal Pals, each being given the guarantee that they would be kept together, through thick and thin. And so they would remain, to the ultimate end.

–

Eliot saw men from his own factory joining up by the score. Clickers and cloggers and clerks. He made up his mind to join them. How could he not, when his country needed him? Besides, he had no family, no wife, no children to consider, and it would be one way of escaping the strangulating hold Lucy and the aunts had upon his life. Eliot realised that he had lost much more than Callum, the adopted son he'd come to love. He'd come to terms with the fact that his beloved wife was dead. He would always love and miss Amelia but life went on and he accepted that fact. She would not have wished him to waste it in endless mourning.

Losing Kate though, was another matter entirely. It had come as a nasty shock how very much he did miss her. Her cheerful presence, the challenging way she would take him to task if she disapproved of something he did or said, that enchanting smile and the teasing gleam in her eye when they had one of their spats. That's what he missed the most, in a way, the little verbal combats they'd had.

He could see now that he might have been a touch hasty in his condemnation of her, made in the heat of the moment when he'd been at his lowest, in the depths of despair. But then he'd never expected her to simply walk out and go back to Poor House Lane. Apparently he'd even said the wrong thing the day he'd taken the doctor to help her through that difficult delivery. Even though he'd swiftly responded to her call for help, she hadn't been in the least bit grateful. And all because he'd asked her to name the father of her child. Wasn't he entitled to know the truth? Could the child indeed be his? He was haunted by the thought that she might be. Why wouldn't the dratted woman tell him?

Kate O'Connor was as obstinate as they come, refusing to answer his questions, or even accept the cottage he'd offered to buy her, although she'd made use of the money he'd sent, he noticed, and set up in competition against him. It felt very much as if she was hell-bent on destroying him.

Worst of all, life was dull now that she was gone, so boring, with the aunts pandering to his every whim. As if on cue, there was Cissie now. He heard her irritatingly gentle scratch upon the door, as if she had no real wish to disturb him but would do so anyway, for how could she get in otherwise, if she didn't knock? And if she didn't scratch on his door, one or other of her pesky dogs did it for her.

'Come in, Aunt Cissie,' Eliot called, striving to keep the irritation out of his voice.

'How did you know it was me?'

He closed his eyes, uttering a silent prayer for patience as she came flustering into the room. She was carrying a tray on which was set a coffee pot, cup and saucer and a small plate of chocolate biscuits. Under her arm were tucked his slippers. He gave a resigned sigh as she set down the tray, pretending to be engrossed in *The Times* so as to avoid further conversation as she proceeded to add milk and sugar to the coffee she painstakingly poured into the cup. Aunt Cissie was fond of finding tidbits of information in the local *Westmorland Gazette* which she thought might amuse him. Unfortunately they were generally concerned with such gems as the county show, which dog had won first prize for obedience, or who had caught some huge fish or other in Lake Windermere or Ullswater, and generally did not interest him in the slightest.

'There you are dear, now see that you drink it while it's hot. Don't let it go cold this time. Shall I put your slippers by the fire to warm?'

Eliot managed to stretch his lips into a smile even as he ground his teeth in frustration. 'As you wish, Aunt. As you wish.' He felt as if he were being suffocated by their goodwill, as if he were choking from lack of air. Every move he made was noted and remarked upon.

'Did you have a nice walk, dear?' they would say when he returned. Or, 'Was it an interesting meeting, dear? I'm afraid your comments at last week's council meeting were not particularly approved of by the *Gazette*.' Wagging a chiding finger as if he were a naughty boy.

And they had an uncanny knack of always knowing where he was and what he was doing, or somehow knew about his movements in advance. 'Isn't it today that you have the meeting about the almshouses?' they would blithely ask, clearly knowing full well. Or, 'Don't be late for the office today, dear. Isn't the accountant coming this morning?' Sometimes, he wondered why they bothered to ask, when they clearly already knew everything about his life down to the last detail.

It was a puzzle to him how they did know. Did they listen at keyholes, or read his diary? He found himself becoming increasingly paranoid about his personal affairs.

They even commented upon every morsel of food he ate, or when he chose to eat it. Should they tell cook that he didn't care for haddock? Would he like something different? Was the time for lunch convenient? Were they correct in assuming that he would not be in for dinner this evening? It was true that he was growing increasingly fond of eating out but Eliot had reached such a level of desperation in an effort to guard his privacy that he would often pretend to be out when really he was hiding in his study, hoping they wouldn't notice. But of course they did notice, and that's when the fetching of small snacks had started, muffins or ham sandwiches, thinking that he'd missed dinner.

So on this occasion he would do his best to remember to drink the dratted coffee, otherwise he'd have to pour it in the aspidistra yet again, which surely did the plant no good at all.

And no doubt tomorrow it would be Vera's turn to wait upon him. The pair fiercely competed with each other to fetch and carry, to bring his whisky, his cigar, his slippers, as if by doing so they could make certain that he wouldn't send them packing, back to their dull lives and their claustrophobic little cottage in Heversham.

If the aunts were a constant source of irritation to him, Lucy was even worse.

Dear Lord, what was he going to do about Lucy? Why he hadn't told her and her spoilt children to leave years ago, he couldn't imagine. But no, that wasn't strictly correct. He knew well enough why he didn't ask her to go. It was all because of a foolish sense of guilt he still nursed over Charles. He'd been compelled to sell both his brother's properties in the end, so how could he? She wasn't entirely to blame for what had happened. She was also a victim of Charles's own greed and stupidity, and of what he had led her to expect, as his wife.

Of course, Charles had been wrong to attempt to perpetrate that fraud but Eliot felt he should have realised how very deeply in debt his brother was, and done more to help him. At the time, he'd believed it was enough to urge him to curb his wife's excesses. Having Lucy live in his house these last five years had taught him how optimistic and unrealistic that hope had been. Money ran through her fingers like water. Yet he still couldn't bring himself to throw her out.

If she was a spendthrift, Eliot felt it incumbent upon himself to attempt to rectify that flaw. He arranged for Lucy to be paid a monthly allowance and set Aunt Vera the task of offering sensible advice on how to manage a budget, thinking that as a very upright, Christian lady, she would make an ideal candidate.

Despite the sale of property, furniture and art, and the steam yacht of course, none having quite brought their true value, there were still an astonishing number of outstanding debts. He'd settled as many as he could, though he'd been forced to ask for time to pay the outstanding balance, due to the financial disasters the company had suffered.

Sadly, none of this succeeded in penetrating Lucy's blithe determination to carry on spending regardless. She simply could not comprehend the skills of good housekeeping, of keeping a check on her expenditure or restraining her needs in any way. Aunt Vera would scold and lecture, cajole and bribe. A case in point recently had been that of Bunty and the dratted new dance shoes.

'No, Aunt Vera, you don't understand. The display is next week and she simply must wear pink, so her old white shoes will not do at all.'

'But why must she wear pink, when she has a perfectly good white pair, and ballet frock to match?'

'It's called a tutu, Aunt, and the white one was for when she was a snowflake. Now she is to be a pink rose.'

'Couldn't she be a white rose?' The faint shadow of a moustache along Aunt Vera's upper lip was very nearly bristling.

'Dear me, no. I really think white was a mistake. Darling Bunty's skin is far too fragile and pale, like mine, for her to look good in white. No, no, it must be pink. Shoes and a new tutu to match.'

'But the last outfit cost a small fortune, and she'll have grown out of it before ever she gets her proper wear from it. Buying a second set so soon is profligate, dear girl. Utterly profligate. Let the child be satisfied with what she has already.'

Lucy responded by going into sulk. 'Really, it would be far more useful if the company made the shoes for her, instead of concentrating entirely upon leather.'

'Don't be foolish. It isn't the job of Tyson's to make ballet pumps for silly little girls. I repeat, let the child be satisfied with white, and have done with the matter.'

'*I want pink! I want pink!*' screamed Bunty, stamping her small feet and going very red in the face.

'Why are we being persecuted in this way? I really can't see what all the fuss is about that a little girl can't be permitted to have a pair of new shoes.' Lucy sobbed above the din.

'*And* a new dress.'

'*Tutu*!'

Bunty lay down on the floor and started to drum her heels in protest until Aunt Vera was almost tearing her hair with frustration, and of course, in the end, caved in and agreed to the purchase of the pink ballet shoes, matching tutu, or whatever other non-essential item was in dispute.

And so the battles continued. Eliot was in despair. His sister-in-law remained as greedy and extravagant as ever, with not the slightest degree of common sense, and short of cutting her off without a penny and turning her from his door to care for her three children as best she may, which of course was utterly unthinkable, he saw little hope of his succeeding where Aunt Vera had failed. Lucy would do as she pleased, and no one seemed to have the power to prevent her.

Chapter Three

Always, after one of these battles, Lucy would storm to her room to expend her tantrum upon her pillows, blaming Eliot, and the aunts. That dratted family really didn't want her around. They didn't even want her precious children.

Darling Bunty was now twelve years old with her mother's ebony hair screwed into inappropriate ringlets, a pale, insipid complexion and small blue-grey eyes that darted about as if afraid of missing something. Even her own mother had to admit that she was not a particularly pretty child, her face and body being too round, almost stocky, with very little grace and beauty. Nor could Lucy deny that her daughter's mouth possessed a decidedly peevish twist to it. Jack, at thirteen, had mouse-brown hair and a weak chin, and he was already growing quite chubby. Very much his father's son. Last but by no means least, came Georgie with his cherubic smile and contradictory behaviour; always full of mischief and naughtiness. At nine years old he had recently started preparatory school, while the two older children had been enrolled into the most expensive academies Lucy could find for them.

'Dear Lord,' Eliot would say whenever she presented him with an account for fees, or sports equipment, riding lessons or whatever. '*How much*? I'm not buying the whole dratted school, am I?' He really was the meanest man imaginable. Far worse even than poor Charles.

Lucy regarded herself as a doting mother. She was always pleased to see her children during the long vacations, wearing though they undoubtedly were, and would beam proudly upon them, pat her son on the head and give her daughter an affectionate peck on the cheek, declaring her delight at seeing them look so well. She would claim to be looking forward to enjoying their company over Christmas, or Easter, but then would sigh with relief when they returned at the end of the vacation, leaving her in peace.

But peace to do what? Without a husband she held no status in the household. It really was quite outrageous that in all of this time she had found no other likely suitor, none rich enough to qualify as one, that is. Nor had Eliot made any effort to find her a husband by introducing her to some of his more affluent friends. He was entirely dilatory in that respect.

But then nothing ever went smoothly where she was concerned.

Look at that dratted whore of Eliot's for a start. Lucy had very cleverly managed to abduct that stupid child of hers and whisk him away so that they'd never find him again, and what had she done? Had she gone into a tearful decline? Not a bit of it. She'd resurrected herself stronger than ever.

Lucy made it her business to keep abreast of everything that went on in that slut's affairs, how she still searched for her child, still asked questions of everyone she met.

At least she'd had the farsightedness to move the boy far away from the workhouse. She'd once visited the farm, over in the Langdales where she'd sent him, sitting in her pony and trap just out of sight under the shade of an over-hanging tree and watched the boy as he'd laboured on the fells. She would have known his bright copper knob anywhere. The farmer had come out at one point and yelled to him across the yard. When the boy hadn't immediately responded, he'd marched over and slapped him about the head before dragging him back to the house by his collar. Oh, Lucy had enjoyed that so much her mouth had positively watered with pleasure. It was perfectly plain that Callum was being treated as a farmhand, not a son of the household, which was exactly what she'd hoped. Satisfied, she'd whipped her horse to a trot and hurried away, entirely happy.

Now, as she sat in her room weeping with frustration, gloomily going over her failing hopes for her own future, the solution came to her. She would marry Eliot. Goodness, why hadn't she thought of this before? By far the best solution. There would be no danger then of his finding another, more fertile wife, or of her own three children not inheriting the business. The tears instantly dried and Lucy set about repairing the damage. Dressing in her finest, diaphanous silk negligee.

She waited until the house was absolutely silent and even the aunts had switched off their light and, so far as she could tell, were fast asleep. Then she went to his room and quietly slipped in without even tapping on his door.

Lucy realised at once that she'd made the most dreadful mistake. You'd have thought she was the wild witch from the dark woods to judge by his reaction as she slid between the sheets beside him. He leapt from the bed as if it were on fire.

'What the hell are you about now, Lucy?'

'I thought it might make sense if we got together. Isn't that what you want, deep down? After all, it's not as if we're blood related. I'm only your sister-in-law, your dead brother's widow. It's not against the law.'

'It's against all laws of decency. For God's sake Lucy, leave my room this minute, and pull yourself together.'

Perhaps rather foolishly, she did not do so. Still believing she could win him, Lucy slid her night-gown from her naked shoulder sufficiently for him to enjoy the ripe fullness of her breasts, regarding him with the kind of provocative lust in her violet eyes that had once excited and entranced Charles, resulting in three handsome children. This thought suddenly brought her to a startled awareness, giving her exactly the ammunition she needed. She wasn't too old for more children, not quite yet.

'Wouldn't you like a child of your own?' she challenged him, crawling across the bed to slide her body up against his, slip her arms about his neck and mouth kisses over his bare chest. Evidently he slept only in his drawers and very fine he looked in them too. His body was leaner, harder and far more exciting than Charles's had ever looked. Her decision to offer herself to him had been for reasons of security only, insurance in a way, but this really might be quite fun. She was surely not without the necessary powers of persuasion to somehow tease or provoke him into having sex with her? And she was perfectly willing to please him in any way he liked. Wasn't she used to all manner of nonsense with dear Charles?

'Aren't you absolutely desperate for a child? Unlike poor dear Amelia, I have proved myself fertile. My children are already Tysons and we could have more. Together. What could be more sensible? You might even enjoy the getting of them, once you stop pining for a dead wife.'

It was as if she had put a light to touch paper. Never, in all her life, had Lucy seen a man so angry. He went white to the lips. So angry was he that she half expected him to physically throw her from his bed, which might have proved rather interesting and erotic, come to think of it. Sadly, instead he snatched up his robe and stalked out of the room, presumably to spend the night on the couch in his study. Lucy didn't set eyes on him again, although she stayed in his bed until Fanny brought in breakfast next morning, and dropped the tray all over the bedroom rug when she found Lucy there, instead of the master.

'You'll never believe what's happened now,' Fanny told Mrs Petty when she scuttled back to the kitchen to collect a second tray of breakfast. But Mrs Petty did believe it, every word, although the tightening of her lips showed that she didn't like it, not one little bit.

As she sliced more bread, wafer thin as madam insisted, and added a scraping of butter, Mrs Petty gave a loud sniff of disapproval. 'I never did like that piece of baggage. Allus did have an eye to the main chance. Too full of herself by half. The poor master would've been much better off with that other one.'

'Which other one?'

'That Kate person, the girl from Poor House Lane. She had more grace in her little finger, than this mucky little madam has in all of her nasty body.'

Dennis paused in the cleaning of the harness and other trappings to think about this for a moment, 'I'd call Miss Lucy's body more tasty than nasty,' and earned a clip round the ear from Fanny, for his trouble.

'Well you would, I suppose,' Fanny told him tartly. Dennis had proved to be a great disappointment to her, never having produced the expected ring or shown any inclination to make their relationship more permanent. She suspected he had a fancy woman somewhere but didn't like to question him too closely on the subject, in case it were true.

'She's doing well for herself an' all these days,' added Mrs Petty, setting a freshly brewed pot of tea on the tray beside the plate of bread and butter.

'Who is?' Fanny picked up the tray and swung away, deliberately turning her back on Dennis to let him see that she didn't care a jot whether he had another woman or not, and certainly had no intention of allowing him a quick fumble at her breasts, as he was so fond of doing. But in her fluster to avoid him, and escape back upstairs before Miss Lucy got in one of her tantrums, she'd quite lost track of the conversation.

'I've just told thee, that other one. Kate whatever she were called.'

'O'Connor. Kate O'Connor.' Dennis said.

'Aye, that's her, that's the one he should have taken up with. Couldn't be any worse than Madam Lucy.'

'Aye, yer right,' Dennis agreed. 'Her business is doing well enough to worry the master. I heard him telling someone in the carriage the other day that she's stopped using a boy on a bicycle for her deliveries. She's bought a van, a big 'un, and means to buy another soon, happen a whole fleet. What do you reckon to that?' His eyes were shining, and

Fanny could see with a rapid sinking of her heart, the thought processes in his daft head. Dennis had always had a passion for mechanical gadgets.

–

The day the van was delivered, Kate's entire work-force turned out to cheer.

'All I need now is someone to drive it,' and found the answer in the shape of Dennis, who turned up on her doorstep the very same day to offer his services.

'I heard you'd bought a motor vehicle and were in need of a driver,' he said, coming straight to the point.

She laughed. 'Gossip still spreads like wildfire round here then. But would you want a job with me?'

'Too right. Even old Askew's gone now, pushing up the daisies, poor old soul, and I'd do owt to get out of that house of nagging women. They're driving me mad.'

Kate made no comment to this, except to offer her condolences over the old gardener. 'Where would you live? There's no accommodation comes with this job.'

'I'll find somewhere, then mebbe Fanny and me can happen get wed at last. She's right fed up that I've done nowt about it so far but that madam has done everything in her power to stop us. Doesn't approve of servants marrying.'

Kate pretended not to understand. 'What madam would that be?'

'Mr Charles's widow, Lucy Tyson. Taken over the place she has, even giving the two aunts a run for their money, which they don't care for at all. Do nothing but squabble over who's in charge, them women do.'

'I did hear that she was living at Tyson Lodge.'

'Oh aye, she's living there right enough. Nicely settled in she is, in every way. Very much so. Not that I don't think the master isn't regretting it. Spends most of the day in the factory, or locked in his study. You couldn't call him entirely happy about the situation but he's got himself lumbered, as you might say. Driven by his own loneliness, I dare say.'

'I see.' There was a small silence while Kate digested the unspoken information Dennis was giving her with his winks and nods and insinuations. She understood well enough what he was trying to tell her, that Eliot was sleeping with his sister-in-law. Information she would much rather not have been privy to, since it made her feel sick to her stomach. Kate drew in a quick, steadying breath, and hardened her heart against any possibility of weakness which might lead to pity. If he was so lonely and unhappy he was driven to the arms of the dreaded Lucy, didn't he deserve to be miserable and harassed to death by women? Serve him right. Hadn't he treated her with heartless cruelty, made her out to be some sort of whore, when all the time he was as bad himself?

Perhaps he would be equally heartless with dear Lucy in the end.

'The job is yours, Dennis, if you want it.'

As well as Dennis, Kate felt confident enough to take on a foreman: someone to keep a better eye on the work in progress. His name was Toby Lynch. Toby was a short, wiry man in his early thirties, with a tousle of blonde hair and a cheery grin.

'Just so's we're clear from the start, I'll stand no nonsense, no messing about with the women, if'n ye catch my drift. Or you'll be out of here faster than a fart from a bottle. Understand?'

He grinned. 'Perfectly. Me mam and two sisters work for you already, so I know how the land lies. I'm grateful you've got 'em out of Swainson's hands.'

Toby soon proved himself capable of the task as he'd had plenty of experience in the shoe trade and, best of all, Kate liked and trusted him, feeling quite safe to leave her precious business in his hands, which released her to go out on the road every day to seek yet more orders. And with Dennis to drive her, she was able to cover a much wider territory as well as carry some stock with her, making deliveries along the way.

-

The farmers' market took place in Kendal every Wednesday. It had been doing so in one form or another since King Richard the Lionheart had first granted the charter back in the twelfth century. The big two-wheeled farmers' carts today, in the spring of 1915, stood in a tidy row the length of the market, and the housewives who walked by would stop to buy butter and eggs, potatoes and green vegetables.

With the business running smoothly and it being May Day, Kate had awarded herself a morning off. She walked along swinging her basket, Flora skipping beside her. The little girl was wearing a pale-blue pinafore, yellow blouse, and a straw bonnet to shade her head from the sun. They'd already watched the Morris Men, and the dancers around the maypole up on the green, though there'd been no beating of the bounds this year because of the war. This was a tradition where the aldermen and burgesses of the borough walked the boundaries of the town, scrambling over walls and ditches in order to do so. The townsfolk would often follow on behind to enjoy the fun. But at least the sun was shining and Kate felt happy and content, enjoying the rare treat of a day out with her child.

'Now isn't this a grand sight? What would you like, my princess? A stick of coltsfoot rock, a glass of lemonade or a twist of candy sugar?'

'Candy sugar, candy sugar, Mammy.'

Laughing, Kate bought the stick of pink candy and gave it to Flora who instantly stuck it in her mouth. 'Don't eat it too fast now. Oh look, I must buy some of these cherries. We could make a delicious pie later. Wouldn't that be fun?'

While Kate waited for the farmer's wife to weigh out the fruit, Flora gazed about her with open curiosity, quickly growing bored as her mother seemed to be taking forever, chatting away to the woman, choosing other items which were not quite such fun, like a turnip, cabbage, potatoes and onions. Sauntering along the line of the carts she came to another which sold entirely butter and eggs, apparently being minded by one red-haired boy.

Flora had been warned not to speak to strangers so she sucked on her sweet, gazing at him wide-eyed, and said nothing. But she could tell by the way his gaze was fastened on the sticky pink candy twist, that he was hungry.

'Give us a lick,' he said at last, his need overcoming good manners.

Flora considered, but she was a kind little girl at heart and began to feel sorry for the boy. He looked nice enough if a bit hot and tired, with a round face and bright copper hair. She broke off the bottom part of her sweet and handed it to him. He snatched it greedily from her and stuffed it into his mouth in one gulp, crunching on the candy so that it was gone in seconds.

'Flora, Flora where are you?'

Flora rolled her eyes. 'That's my mammy.'

The boy stepped forward for a better look. 'Who, the one with red hair? She looks nice.'

Flora let out an exasperated sigh. 'I suppose so. A bit of a fusspot. Won't let me do anything or go anywhere, but you know how mothers are.'

'No, I don't, s'matter of fact. I haven't got a mother.'

Flora's eyes stretched wider. 'No mother? Don't talk soft, everybody has a mother.'

'Well I don't. I'm an orphan, see. I live on t'farm with Mr and Mrs Brocklebank.'

'Flora, where are you?'

'Got to go,' and spinning on her heels, Flora skipped happily back to where Kate stood waiting for her, her basket heavy with produce.

Grabbing the child's hand, she gave her daughter a little shake. 'What do you think you were doing wandering off like that? That was very naughty. Haven't I told you to stay by me?'

'I was only talking to that boy.'

'Never mind what you were doing. You do what I say and stick by my side. Is that clear?'

Flora silently nodded, and with her hand clasped firmly in her mother's, meekly fell into step beside her, glancing back only once when they reached the end of the street. The boy was still watching them and Flora lifted a hand to wave goodbye.

'Who are you waving to?' Kate asked, feeling guilty at her overreaction. The child had only gone to the next-but-one cart, not even out of sight. She really must allow her some freedom and not be so consumed by the fear of losing her. She turned now

42

to see who it was who had caught her daughter's attention, but saw no one of particular importance at all, other than a fat farmer's wife berating her child by clipping him about the head. Poor boy. What had he done to deserve such a cluttering, she wondered. How cruel some mothers were.

She smiled down at Flora, who was looking quite distressed over the little scene, and attempted to distract her. 'Come along, my precious, we shall go home and make cherry pie, then eat the lot.'

Kate didn't notice when the young boy wriggled free to escape the thrashing, and ran after her for some distance, at least until she'd turned into Finkle Street, where he stopped and stood by the lamp post and watched her walk away, still laughing and chattering to her pretty little daughter, until she'd quite vanished from sight.

-

A few weeks later, Fanny walked into Kate's workshop with a swagger. It amused Kate to see the housemaid flush with embarrassment as she came towards her. 'What a joy it is to see you again, Fanny, and looking so well. What're you doing in my neck of the woods?'

Fanny glowered, the cheeks flushing pinker than ever, for this Kate O'Connor cut a very different figure from the one whose feet had been filthier than her own boots all those years before. She was no longer a nursemaid, but an employer, one who deserved increasing respect in the town. And Fanny needed work. 'I'm all right, I suppose, but me and Dennis, we're not gerrin' wed. He's tekken up with some shop assistant or other. Right little floozy, she is.'

'Oh dear, I'm sorry to hear that, I am so.' Since Dennis was her driver, Kate was well aware of his new domestic arrangements, but thought it best not to admit as much at this juncture.

'Don't be. I'll survive. Only I'll ring his flamin' neck and throttle him if the Hun don't do it first.'

Kate nodded sympathetically, waiting patiently for whatever Fanny had come to say. When still she hesitated, showing no sign of coming to the point, she was forced to prompt her with, 'So what can I do for ye on this bright morning?'

The housemaid cleared her throat. 'The fact is Kate – er – Miss er – um.'

'Kate will do fine.'

Now that she'd finally started it all came out in a rush, on one swift indrawn breath. 'The fact of the matter is Mr Tyson has decided to take the King's shilling and be an officer and I can't stand being a housemaid no longer, not in that house. I'm fed up with all the work and being bossed about, and me wages haven't gone up in years. What with old Mr Askew dead, and Dennis gone, that leaves Mrs Petty, me and daft Ida to look after that big place and the two aunts. Not forgetting madam herself, of course, who never lifts a finger. So I'm not stopping on. I've had enough.'

Kate's recollection of what Fanny had told her got stuck somewhere around the part where she'd said Eliot had joined up. Dear God, no, don't let him do that!

'By heck, I don't mind telling you, Kate, 'cause I know you'll understand but she's a right one and no mistake. A nastier piece of work you wouldn't find in a long day's march. Why, just the other day she made me clean and black-lead all the grates twice over because she said I hadn't done 'em proper. She called me a lazy slut. Lazy my eye, when I spend me bleeding life on me knees in that house, and not saying prayers neither. And you know what I caught her up to t'other morning…'

Kate had heard enough servant's gossip. 'You say Mr Tyson has joined up. When did he do that? When does he leave?'

'Sometime in the next week or two, I imagine, off to do his training first though. Anyroad, like I were saying…'

Kate set her hands flat on the desk top, since they'd started to tremble, and leaning closer, fixed the girl with a stern glare. 'Fanny, I haven't all day to sit here listening to your tittle-tattle. What is it, exactly, that you are wanting from me? Would it be a job by any chance?'

The housemaid looked shame-faced but admitted that it was. 'I'm looking for a fresh start, a new beginning. I thought you might help me to get one, since we're old chums like.'

Kate thought this description a somewhat exaggerated view of their relationship but made no comment on Fanny's assessment. 'You know, of course, that Dennis is working for me too. Would that not bother you, in view of your current differences? Because I don't want any trouble, Fanny. I don't want you imagining you can win him back, and then causing mischief when you don't succeed.'

Fanny's cheeks flared bright crimson, for of course winning him back had indeed been on her mind, but her voice was quite steady as she told her lie. 'I wouldn't have him back if he were wrapped up in a parcel and tied with a scarlet ribbon. No, I'm finished wi' men. And I'm done wi' being an housemaid an' all.'

Kate was still doubtful, remembering the way the girl had sent her to Coventry. She'd been so imperious in her manner, as if she were God's gift and Kate something the cat had dragged in. Yet she didn't blame her for wanting to better herself. Domestic service was a thankless task, particularly working for the likes of Lucy Tyson, and she'd earn much more money in the workshop. 'I'm not taking anyone on at the moment but since you and I are – as you say – old chums in a manner of speaking, I'll make an exception in your case. You can start tomorrow in the tongue department.'

'Oh Kate… oh thank you, miss, thank you. I'm that grateful.' Fanny's eyes shone and for one dreadful moment Kate thought she might actually be about to hug her, but then she hastily backed away. Yet the girl's obvious joy brought a smile to Kate's lips. There were many kinds of abuse, and perhaps Madam Lucy had bullied this lass once too often. Fanny deserved a chance too, just as much as the women in Poor House Lane.

'That's settled then. You can go now. I'll see you in the morning, sharp at seven.'

'Yes miss.' It was only when she reached the door that Fanny thought to ask, 'What's the tongue department? What do I have to do there?'

'Certainly not use your own tongue, Fanny. We can hear quite enough of that at other times.'

She had the grace to giggle.

'I've girls to make the eyelets in the boots, others to put in the lining if there is one, some to fold the leather in a process called skiving, while others close up and stitch the toe. You, Fanny, will join the girls whose task it is to put in the tongue. But don't worry, you'll be given very clear instructions tomorrow, so don't be late.'

As Fanny dashed off, thoroughly pleased with herself, Kate sank back into her chair before her knees quite gave way. She just hoped that she'd done the right thing and that Fanny would suit, and change her mind about throttling poor Dennis. Yet all she really cared about was that Eliot was leaving. *He would soon be going to war.*

Chapter Four

Lucy slammed down her knife and fork in a fury. As if things weren't bad enough, Eliot had taken it into his head to play the hero. It had come like a bolt from the blue when he'd made the announcement over dinner, quite ruining her appetite. She hadn't even guessed that he intended to enlist which meant that he'd escape her clutches just when she'd thought of capturing him.

Lucy was against the war; had joined the Women's Peace League to raise money for the cause, campaigning for it to be stopped. However genuine the emotions of the other pacifists, Lucy was simply concerned with the disruption to her own life. And she'd had quite enough of that already.

The aunts, fools that they were, entirely supported Eliot's decision. 'Quite right, dear chap,' Aunt Vera said, pursing her mouth into a prim line of approval. 'The right and proper thing for a gentleman to do is join the call to arms.'

'Oh, indeed,' agreed her sisterly echo, patting and stroking the dog leaning against her with great excitement.

But it was Lucy who gave a small growl of annoyance, which Aunt Vera heard. 'What did you say, dear?'

'I said, how can Eliot be so foolish as to enlist when he is needed here, to run the company? How are we supposed to manage without him? Who on earth will run the business while you're away, playing the hero?' she demanded, fixing him with an icy glare. 'Surely you don't expect me to keep an eye on things for you?'

Eliot gave Lucy a cool, distancing smile. 'I've made the necessary arrangements. And no, you will not be troubled. I have my accounts clerk to deal with the day to day issues of paying wages and outstanding bills, including, dear sister-in-law, your own allowance, so you will not be inconvenienced in any way. Although I would remind you that there is a war on, and prudence and thrift are the order of the day.'

'Poppycock, I'm not letting some jumped up little Hun ruin my life. Isn't it bad enough that I have no home of my own and am forced to live on handouts and charity?' Lucy felt trapped, stifled, living here with the two dragons, as she privately thought of the aunts. She'd been patient long enough. She wanted, *deserved*, a home of her own, a husband and money in the bank to see her comfortable and secure. She wasn't old like them, but still young with more than half of her life still to be lived and enjoyed. She should never have been deprived of the house on Stramongate, she thought, quite forgetting that it had been her own decision to move into Tyson Lodge, not to mention her own reckless spending which had put both her homes in jeopardy.

'Why don't you do something to stop that girl from destroying us? Why don't you fight back and beat her at her own game? Surely, with the power of Tyson's name, it would be an easy matter to put her out of business.'

'By *that girl*, I assume you mean Kate O'Connor?'

'I mean that no good chit of a whore, the girl who sold you her own child and then lost him through her habitual carelessness.'

Eliot winced at her bluntness, biting back an instinctive urge to defend Kate for hadn't he accused her of the self-same thing in the past? Yet he felt honour-bound to speak, for nothing of the sort had been proved and he'd lived to regret his hasty judgement of her. 'I'm not sure that is correct. And however irritating, her business is nothing more than normal, healthy competition. She has substantial orders from the army and is even now negotiating a contract with the Russian government.'

'Tch, the woman must sleep with every Tom, Dick and Harry in order to achieve so much, so quickly. She's a self-seeking slut...'

Lucy went on talking, going on and on about Kate O'Connor but Eliot had stopped listening. He felt thoroughly wearied of women. He'd be glad to get away and be in the company of men for a change, war or no war.

'... You could at least stop being so damned honourable. She's deliberately set out to ruin you. Any fool can see that. Having stolen Dennis, Fanny's gone to work for her now. She's taking us over. Why you allow her to get away with it, is quite beyond me. I would've thought you'd have put your own niece and nephews first.'

'If that is another complaint about money, may I simply say in my own defence that I hope that I do my duty, what I believe to be right. However, my pockets are not bottomless pits overflowing with brass, Lucy. Times are hard.'

How tired she was of hearing those words. 'Kate O'Connor is doing well enough, despite the war, stealing business from Tyson's hand over fist. So why aren't you doing something about it, instead of running away?' His lack of response to this barb as he continued to eat his meal, even politely commenting on the tenderness of the beef and making Cissie flush with pride at the compliment, infuriated Lucy all the more.

That damned nursemaid was making her advancement at their expense, and Eliot didn't seem to care whether there would be a business left for them to inherit. Why didn't he do something to stop her? Lucy felt a rage building up inside. She could taste the sourness of it in her throat like bile. She refused to allow this dreadful family to treat her so callously, as if she were of no account. Not for one moment had she imagined her life would turn out this way, stuck at the Lodge as some sort of dependant relative with no say over what went on. She was the mother of three children who should join this business one day. And it was surely her task, as their mother, to ensure that there was something worthwhile for them to take over in the fullness of time, particularly considering all the trouble she'd taken. She needed to make that point clear at least. 'If you weren't so selfish, you would provide me with a home of my own. Don't my children deserve that much, at least?'

'I was under the impression that your children were very well provided for. They certainly cost enough.' Eliot sighed as he reached for the wine decanter to refill his glass, a rather fine claret, though how much longer he would be able to afford such luxuries was a moot point.

'That *you* resent paying for.'

'That's not what he said, Lucy,' Aunt Vera chipped in. 'Dear Eliot is merely advocating prudence.'

'And thrift,' echoed Aunt Cissie, slipping a delicate slice of beef to her favourite dog.

'What about my precious darlings? Don't they deserve the very best of care? You destroyed their father, would you destroy them too?'

'My word, Lucy, that's a bit below the belt,' Aunt Vera sternly reprimanded her in vinegar tones. 'We all know that Charles was the author of his own misfortune, as are you my dear, to a degree.'

'I beg your pardon?'

Eliot patiently flapped a hand to calm heated tempers. Poor Vera was puffing like an old steam train and he rather expected steam to rise from her ears at any moment. 'Speaking for myself, I can't help admiring Kate O'Connor's tenacity and entrepreneurial spirit but fear not, it might be a struggle but Tyson's will survive. One cannot expect to have things all one's own way in business. Matters could change radically after the war. The army won't require so many boots and she might be the one in difficulties, whereas Tyson's will have its classic lines to fall back on.'

'There you are, Lucy dear,' said Aunt Vera with waspish satisfaction. 'You will simply have to be patient.'

Lucy smiled at the older woman with all the sweetness of acid.

–

Fanny took to her new job without any problems whatsoever, finding it quite a treat to be with girls her own age. And to Kate's enormous relief, she paid no attention whatsoever to Dennis, walking past him in tight-lipped silence, with her nose in the air in that stuck-up way of hers. Kate wondered how Mrs Petty and Ida would cope without housemaid, gardener or chauffeur, doubting they'd manage to replace any of them just now. Coping with the aunts would not be easy, and who would Lucy find to boss? Not that it had anything to do with her what went on at Tyson Lodge. She had her own problems to think of, after all, but she was finding it difficult to concentrate on practical concerns today. All Kate could think of was that Eliot had enlisted. She sat plaiting her daughter's hair, listening to her chatter on about what her teacher had thought about a picture she'd drawn, what she was going to do today in school and how many gold stars she'd won lately.

A small hand tugged at her sleeve. 'Mammy, are you listening? I want to go to Maggie's for tea. Will you let me?'

'Of course, darling, if her mother is happy to have you.'

'Oh, she is, she is. We're going to make jam tarts. Maggie's mummy does things like that with her all the time.'

Not like me, Kate thought, with a nudge of motherly guilt. 'Well, perhaps Maggie's mummy doesn't have to go out to work, as I do.'

'Course she don't. Maggie's got a daddy to do that.' Flora shook her head, making the streaks of fire in her dark auburn curls dance and bounce with health. The child was vain enough to be constantly demanding that they be allowed to fall loose on her shoulders in soft waves, but Kate insisted that plaits were far more practical. Then as if asking the question for the first time, which wasn't the case at all, 'Why don't I have a daddy?'

'Oh my, now look at the time. Aren't we going to be late, if we don't get a move on.' Callum had been too young to understand that his daddy was dead, that he was never coming back from the river. It had been easy to talk of heaven, and Jesus needing him more, since he didn't fully appreciate the finality of death. It seemed to be much more difficult with Flora, who was a child filled with questions and curiosity. But how could she tell her the truth, when she couldn't bring herself to even admit that Eliot was her father.

Kate found the image of Flora's pretty little face blurring as her eyes filled with unexpected tears. Flora's daddy was going to France to fight and she didn't even know it. Dear God, how would *she* survive, not knowing how or where he was, not even able to write to find out if he was still alive? Kate wanted to hate him, but she couldn't. She wanted never to think of him again, never to need him, but that seemed impossible. She felt trapped by the weakness of her own emotions.

Flora said, 'And will we go to the market soon? I want another candy twist, and to see my friend again.'

'And what friend is that?' Kate said with a laugh. 'Now will ye fetch yer coat, or your teacher will give you a black mark, not a gold star.'

'The one I shared my sweet with. You know, I told you, the boy on the farmer's cart with the red hair.'

Kate felt as if she had been drenched in cold water. But if so, then why did she instantly feel all hot and prickly, her fingers going numb so that they became paralysed, unable to fasten the buttons on her daughter's coat.'

'Let me do it Mammy. You're so *slow*,' Flora complained.

'Where did you see him, this boy? How old was he? What did he look like? Which cart was it? Did it have a name on it? What was the farmer called?'

But these were too many questions for Flora. Besides, she'd grown tired of the conversation, was far more engrossed with showing off her new-found skill with buttons. 'Mammy look, I can nearly do shoelaces too. My teacher says I'm the cleverest girl in the class.'

'Flora, listen to Mammy. I want you to try to remember. How old would you say the boy was?'

It took some time and a great deal of patience before Kate could get anything more out of her. 'Oh, I don't know. He was bigger than me. And he was hungry. That fat lady hit him.'

And then an image of the fat farmer's wife clouting a boy about the head, whom she'd taken to be the woman's own son, came into her mind and a wave of sickness hit her. Had that been Callum? Could it possibly have been him? Oh dear God, had she been so near, and never realised it was him? Oh, let it not be him. Much as she longed to find him, let him not be so ill-treated.

Kate walked her daughter to school that day, as she did every morning, but this time, instead of hurrying back to the workshop to get on with the mass of orders and tasks piled up on her desk, she dashed to the town hall in a frenzy of agitation, demanding to speak to councillors, to the Town Clerk, to anyone who could tell her the names of the farmers who attended the market. She was told only that it was a free market. That farmers came and went at will.

–

For the last five years Kate had studiously managed to avoid Eliot Tyson, catching no more than the odd glimpse of him at a distance, for all Kendal was a small town. She hadn't wanted to see him. The mere sight of him had served only to bring back all the pain of loving him, and the agony of losing Callum.

Occasionally, she'd see the two aunts going into the post office on Finkle Street or shopping on Branthwaite Brow. And once or twice she'd spotted Lucy marching into Berry's Drapers on Highgate, her three children trailing after her like a line of ducklings being led to the slaughter. But Kate always made sure that none of them ever saw her.

She also made a point of steering clear of the far side of the river, where she'd be sure to run across him. Yet Kate was ever aware that he was not too far away. On her way back from her fruitless errand to the Town Hall, she looked across the river to the grey stone, square mansion, to the turrets and windows that she'd once known so well, imagining him closeted in his study, a fire burning in the grate, a book on his lap. But no, he would be taking breakfast with the aunts and Lucy, before hurrying on to his work, as she should be doing. She'd often hoped and prayed that he might be missing her, that he was lonely too, yet telling herself that he deserved to be so for rejecting her so heartlessly. That he might, perhaps, come looking for her one day. But of course he never had, and in the end she'd come to see that it was foolish to go on hoping, telling herself she didn't want him anyway.

Didn't she hate him for choosing Lucy over her? Wasn't she at least *trying* to hate him, and to prove that she could stand on her own two feet. And damn it, hadn't she succeeded? Until now.

Should she tell him about this possible sighting? Did she need his help? Maybe later, when she had more information.

She went to the market place, empty today, it not being the right day, but she visited all the shops asking shopkeepers if they had seen a red-haired boy minding a cart with a fat farmer's wife. None had. No one knew the name. None could help her.

Kate stood in helpless misery and wept. If only she had paid more attention at the time to what

Flora had been saying. If only she'd gone back to remonstrate with the woman for clouting the boy. But she'd thought it none of her business. Didn't it happen all the time, mother's chastising their sons. It didn't necessarily mean that he was being ill-treated, or that he was unhappy. Or even that it was Callum. There must be any number of other red-headed boys in Westmorland. But somehow, in her heart of hearts, she knew that it was him, that this was a clue, and she felt a kernel of excitement despite her despair. How many farmers were there in this county? Not so many surely that she couldn't find him. All she had to do was visit all the other markets. Ambleside, Buttermere, Coniston, Keswick, Kirkby Lonsdale, wherever farmers gathered to sell their produce. Somewhere amongst them, she would find him.

Wasting no time, she ran to find Dennis. 'Forget the deliveries today. I have a more important job for us to do.'

'Are you sure, Kate? That Mr Rumley don't like to be kept waiting, and Joseph Webster is a stickler for his boots being delivered on time, even to the hour. He'll have his lads on standby, waiting to unpack the boxes the minute we arrive.'

'Well, he'll be disappointed today.' She was flying around, answering queries, giving out hasty instructions, calling for Millie, wanting to tell her friend what she'd discovered. When she succeeded in finding her, gabbling out her tale at breathless speed,

Millie's eyes opened wide in wonder. She hugged Kate tight, instantly promised to collect Flora from school and keep an eye on things here, and sent Kate on her way with all her love.

'I shall have every finger crossed. Bring him home, Kate. Bring him home.'

They drove miles that day, through town after town, it seemed as if it might be the length and breadth of the county, though how could it be, pottering along far too slowly for Kate's liking, and with far too many stops. Dennis would need to refill the tank with petroleum, mend a puncture or simply cool down the engine. It was an exhausting trip and utterly fruitless as it turned out. Either there was no market that day, or no sign of a red-haired boy with or without a fat farmer's wife. It was near midnight by the time they arrived back home again, tired and discouraged.

'We can try another day,' Dennis consoled her, fully understanding what it was all about by this time. 'But not tomorrow. We have to deliver those boots.'

They tried again a few days later, deliveries or no, sadly with equal lack of success. And as if this wasn't bad enough, on Sunday a train was leaving with the next batch of recruits off for training. No doubt Eliot would be amongst them.

The last thing she wanted was for him to go to France and run the risk of being killed. Kate couldn't begin to contemplate a world without him, a time when she didn't know that one day, whether or not their differences were ever settled, she couldn't at least see him about town and know that he was safe and well. However much she might deny it, didn't she love him still? Wouldn't she always love him, drat the man.

There was no question in her mind but that she would have to go on Sunday and see him off. How could she escape it? But not for a moment would she allow him to see that she cared.

–

Kate could see at once that Eliot was surprised to see her. He stood on the station platform in his smart overcoat, his bag at his feet, and looked at her as if he couldn't believe what his eyes were telling him.

'Is it really you, Kate? You look well.'

'Thank you.' She'd made sure that she did look well. She was dressed in a brand new burgundy coat and ankle-length skirt, a pale blue silk jabot at the throat and a matching hat with a long feather atop her neatly coiffured head. She'd bought the outfit especially for the occasion and the open admiration in his warm brown eyes was gratifying, if painful to witness. She came briskly to the point. Without removing her black kid gloves, she handed him an envelope. 'I heard you were going off on training today and wanted to bring you this. It's the return of the money you loaned me.'

'Good lord, Kate, that wasn't a loan.'

'Well, I've treated it as such. I'm a decent, hard-working woman, and I don't take money from men, not even gentlemen.' She met his startled gaze unblinking. Kate had every intention of keeping this meeting strictly formal. Not for a moment must he be allowed to guess the inner turmoil she was suffering.

'I'm sure you don't. I mean – I never thought that you...'

'I wanted to make that quite clear, considering our past circumstances. And there was one other thing I thought you should know. A young boy was spotted on the market place the other day, a boy with red hair. I don't know whether it's Callum or not, as I haven't been able to find him yet. But I intend to keep searching, just in case. I've already visited quite a few other markets, to no avail, but I'll keep looking. I wanted you to know that – before you went away. I won't give up, and I'll tell the aunts, if I get any news. Now, I wish you well, a safe homecoming and bid you good day.'

She turned on her heel, had walked for some yards before he came out of his stunned paralysis and in two long strides was by her side, looking as if he might snatch hold of her arm but then seemed to think better of it.

'Kate, don't rush away. I can't believe what you're saying. You think it might be him?'

She gave a helpless shrug. 'I can't be sure till I find the boy. It might all be a waste of time. I've followed up so many leads already, but there's always a chance, don't you think?'

'The trouble is, Kate, he'll have changed so much by now. He's a grown boy, almost a young man, so how can we know what he'll even look like? All these lost years! So much we've missed, been deprived of. He won't have that soft baby voice any more, nor your Irish lilt in it. He won't giggle and chuckle as he used to do. He could look and sound like a Westmorland farmer. He might not even be in the county.'

'Oh, don't say that. Don't I drive around in me pony and trap every Sunday, just on the off chance I might spot him. And day after day I've had Dennis drive me over half the county in the van, when really we should be working. If he's here, I'll find him, so I will.'

Neither of them mentioned the possibility of his being dead. They never had and never would. Not until a body was found to prove it, Callum would remain forever a lost child.

As she turned her eyes up to his, he saw the anguish written in their grey depths, the need for reassurance, and something more.

Impulsively, Eliot took her hand and squeezed it. 'If anyone can find Callum, you can. But please don't go, not like this. At least wait till the train departs. I'd like to see you standing there, on the platform, when it draws out of the station. Will you do that for me?'

She looked sideways up at him, at the pleading in his eyes, shielding her own with a sweep of long, golden lashes. She'd meant to be entirely practical and businesslike, to simply return the money, inform him of this new lead which she was desperately trying not to get too hopeful about, and walk away. But soon, when the short training was over, he would be off to the front. Tommy Hodgson had gone to France and never returned. What if the same thing were to happen to Eliot and she never saw him again either? How would she feel about refusing this very simple request? How would she ever be able to live with herself? Kate felt herself weakening. 'Very well.'

'We've time for a cuppa, I think. Would you care for one?'

Chapter Five

Kate sat almost in a trance, oddly drained of emotion, feeling spent and exhausted, unable to think of a thing to say.

'So, tell me, how you are doing, Kate. How is the baby – er – how is she?'

It was astonishing, though typical of him, that he should start by asking about her child and not the business. They sat on a bench in the teeth of a cold wind, since the tea rooms were heaving with young men and their families, and drank their tea to the strains of *Tipperary* played by the town band. Kate could see the Mayor in his robes and chain, and what were presumably various members of his corporation all walking about, trying to look important as they reassured men that they would not lose out by volunteering, that their families would be looked after and well provided for.

She kept her spine stiff, her hands clasped tight on the cup and saucer, as if to a lifeline. 'Flora is grand, ta very much. And she's not a baby now, but quite the little schoolgirl. She's been attending a kindergarten on Aynam Road but last September she started school proper, which she loves.'

'Splendid, splendid.' He looked slightly nonplussed, thrown off-balance by her self-assurance and cool control. Perhaps he half expected her to be scratching his eyes out, or weeping with anguish all over him. Kate heard him clear his throat, as if he didn't know quite what to say next; noticed from the corner of her eye how he glanced up and down the crowded platform, and down at the still unopened envelope in his hand. He slipped it into a pocket of his great coat. 'I've maintained an interest in your progress. I heard you were doing well, that you were very busy.'

'Indeed I am, as no doubt ye are yourself.'

He gave a snort of laughter, one which held not a trace of humour in it. 'As you well know, busy is not the word I would choose to describe Tyson's these days. I'm sure you are only too aware of the damage you've inflicted upon my firm, Kate O'Connor, so don't pretend otherwise. But then wasn't that your intention all along? The ship won't go down, but it is badly holed and taking in water. We are a shadow of our former selves.'

She opened her eyes very wide as she stared innocently up at him. 'Indeed I'm shocked to hear ye say so.'

Had she done it then? She'd beaten him, or at least wounded him badly. So why wasn't she feeling that warm glow of satisfaction she'd expected to feel? Why didn't she experience the pure joy of triumph? 'I'd've thought you'd be doing grand, what with the war and all. Still, I'm sure you'll manage to survive, Tyson's allus do.' She turned her head away and sipped her tea, to prove that she really wasn't interested in whether he did or not, or even if he answered her question.

Eliot gave of snort of disbelief, exhaling a breath that clouded to mist in the cool morning air. 'Oh, we'll survive. I'll make damn sure of it, even if you did snap up all orders to supply the army with the boots they need, a good twelve months before I even thought to ask. Very forward-thinking of you.'

And now her lovely mouth curled into a tiny smile, relishing her victory, and Kate's clear grey eyes gleamed with delight to see how his jaw tightened with annoyance at being bested by a woman. 'I believe it was you yourself, Eliot Tyson, who carefully explained it all to me. I didn't properly understand, me being only a simple servant girl at the time, but later I got to thinking it might make good business sense, so decided to give it a go. And I must say, the officer I spoke to regarding the order was a perfect gentleman, smothered in badges and ribbons so he was, but still he made time to talk to me.'

Eliot sighed. 'I don't doubt it. Bowled over by that enchanting smile, I shouldn't wonder. No doubt you made him an offer he couldn't refuse?'

'I did indeed give him a price that was beneficial to us both, if that's what yer meaning. But then what else would you expect me to offer?' Kate tartly responded.

'I wouldn't know, Kate, would I? Depends what you considered you had of value at the time, or what you thought might be of interest to him. I'm sure whatever deal you cut, it was to your advantage.'

She could feel a surge of anger at the insinuation beneath his words, as if he were implying that she would offer herself, or her child, if it was politic to do so. Her fingers tightened on the cup in her hand as she struggled to stay calm but they must have been shaking after all, because some of the tea spilled over on to her lap. She leapt to her feet, dabbing at it in annoyance with her handkerchief. 'Oh no, me new skirt!'

'Can I help?' he offered, and she slapped his hand away.

'I can manage perfectly well, thank you.' It certainly wouldn't do to let him see that he had scored a point and rattled her. Ignore him, the voice in her head urged. He was as arrogant as ever, always so damned sure he was right. Best to pretend you haven't properly understood. She sat down again, trying to disguise the small damp stain on her lap by pulling her coat close about her. 'In any case, I don't believe my business methods are any concern of yours.'

'They are certainly nothing if not individual, and largely seem to involve theft of some sort.'

'Theft?'

'Of *my* customers.'

She opened her mouth to deny it but then closed it again, nipping her lower lip between her teeth, firmly resolved to say nothing more. He was probably right. She had stolen a great many of his customers.

He sipped his tea, which suddenly tasted sour and unpalatable, so he set it aside, brow puckering into a troubled frown. Leaning his elbows on his knees, he deliberately kept his gaze turned away from her, though even when staring at the ground, he could see her trim ankles and her small neat feet in their fashionable button boots.

He sat back, unable to bear being so near to her and yet find a brick wall still stood between them. 'It's a pity, in a way, that we don't get on, that we spend so much time at loggerheads. It would make more sense if we were on the same side. I'm sure then we could help each other a good deal, if we but tried. Particularly now, with the war on, and my business needing more attention than I can give it.

'Who's taking care of it then, the business? Holy Mother, yer not leaving that bloomin' foreman in charge?'

'I must do my duty, Kate. What else can I do?'

'You're mad. Why do you stubbornly insist on trusting him?'

'Who else can I trust?'

'Me. You could trust me.'

He gave a nostalgic smile, the warmth in his eyes cooling to the chill of polished marble. 'That might have been true once, but not now Kate, not any more. Why would I risk handing over the running of my business to the woman who has deliberately set out to destroy it? The woman who has stolen not only many of my workers, but some of my best customers by ruthlessly and constantly undercutting me on price.'

'I offer a much faster service. And where was *your* support, when I needed it? Isn't it every man, or woman, for themselves? And if your workers leave you, you should perhaps ask yourself why.'

He frowned, looking thoughtful for a moment, the first shadow of doubt creeping in. Then he cast another glance in her direction, noting the sweep of those fine lashes, the curve of her flushed cheek, the proud way in which she held herself, and something strange happened deep inside him, a clenching of muscles, a burning sensation, so that he was forced to look away. Just because she was a beauty, didn't mean a thing, he told himself. Of course he wanted her, what man wouldn't? And he couldn't get it out of his head that many others had probably enjoyed her too, just as he had. He'd no proof of her innocence. She'd certainly produced two children with comparative ease, and God knows who their respective fathers were.

She'd climbed into his own bed without a moment's hesitation. Young Dennis had been sufficiently besotted to leave secure employment to go and work for her, and wouldn't hear a word said against her. According to rumour, she'd enjoyed any number of suitors in recent years and had now taken on a foreman, Toby somebody-or-other, who she was probably getting cosy with. For all he knew, she might not ever have been married, since her husband had been conveniently dead – drowned apparently, when he'd first met her. He hated himself for being jealous, but was it any wonder?

'You're probably right. It wouldn't be appropriate for us to work together.'

'And I'm doing fine on me own, thanks all the same.' One moment she moved towards him, then he'd lost her again.

'And at least you don't have to see Swainson every day.'

She gave a small smile. 'That is a bonus, yes.'

'You must have liked him once-over, to dally with him as you did.'

She turned wide, disbelieving eyes upon him. 'Dally with Swainson? Sweet Jaysus, I'd cut me own throat first.'

'He has implied that his advances were once willingly accepted, presumably until that little contretemps over pay, when you believed he'd rebuffed you. Isn't that why you've had it in for him so fiercely all these years, out of some need for feminine vengeance?'

'If he told ye all that, then he's a bigger liar than I gave him credit for, and you a bigger fool to believe him.'

'Is that so?'

There it was again. The old arrogance back in place, the cold superiority of his expression telling her they were as far apart as ever. Kate set down her cup and saucer with a sharp click on the bench beside her, a great wedge of tears blocking her throat. She was near drowning in tea, having had two cups already while she waited for him to arrive. Oh, but why could he not trust her? 'Believe what you like, you're obviously determined to see me in worst possible light.'

Eliot again felt confused and uncertain of his ground. He told himself that he would have stood by his decision to sack Swainson, had he thought it would do any good, if he'd believed for one moment that her accusation over his abuse of women could possibly be true. But he only had her word for that, no evidence to back it up. From the moment Swainson had said, no – implied – they'd once been lovers, he'd had no doubts about the decision. The Union had not found it difficult to convince him to do nothing. He'd wanted to believe in her innocence but how could he, when she'd been more concerned with her own welfare than the safety of her own child? If she hadn't been fussing over this foolish vendetta with Swainson, Callum might still be living safe and well at Tyson Lodge to this day. He could very easily hate her when he put his mind to it.

Yet he wanted her too. God, how he wanted her.

A silence had fallen between them, long and awkward. Desperately needing to break it, Eliot changed the subject. 'Once I've completed the initial training, I'll be allowed home for a few days before being shipped overseas, in order to sort out my affairs. Will I see you again?'

Kate deliberately kept her heart hard, a piece of granite with sharp edges even if its core might be soft as mallow. 'I very much doubt it. And I'm sure you'll have enough to see to, without bothering about me. Won't you want to spend time with Lucy? I'm surprised she didn't come to see you off today.' There, she'd said it. Now he would know how she too listened to gossip.

He gave a snort of laughter, as if she'd said something amusing. 'I do assure you that Lucy would be the last person I would want to see. I can't wait to escape her greedy talons, and if she did come to see me off, it would only be to give me her latest shopping list, or yet more bills to pay. The woman drives me demented.'

She glanced up at him, stunned. 'Then you're not – I mean, you and she… I heard that you…'

He frowned. 'I haven't the first idea what tales you've been listening to, Kate, but I do assure you there is nothing between my sister-in-law and myself but tiresome duty.'

So he wasn't sleeping with her, after all? Kate found herself smiling. 'Looks like we both have a habit of jumping to conclusions.'

He regarded her thoughtfully for a moment. 'It would seem so. I do assure you that if I could find some way to prise her, and the blessed aunts, out of my house, I would do so.'

Kate suddenly felt so ridiculously lightheaded that she actually giggled. 'I could lend you a lever, or mebbe you could change the locks when they're out on their calls.'

'Now why didn't I think of that?'

'Oh, drat, there's the train whistle.' Her whole body jerked, face naked with fear and his startled gaze took in the horror she clearly felt over his imminent departure into unknown dangers.

'I'll be fine,' he soothed, as if she had spoken these thoughts out loud.

Kate cleared her throat and gave him what she hoped was a cool and distant smile, keeping her tone brisk. 'Course ye will. Only the good die young,' and then she gulped, realising what she'd said and unable to prevent herself, leaned over and kissed him quickly on the cheek.

He seemed startled but then smiled at her, a smile warm enough to soften any woman's heart. Any, that is, but Kate O'Connor's. 'Thank you for coming. And for that kiss. I'm not sure I deserve it.'

She felt flustered now, wishing she'd managed to stay calm, but his reaction to her mention of Lucy had quite unnerved her, set her pulses racing. 'I'm quite sure you don't, but everyone else seems to be getting one, so we can't have you feeling left out, now can we?' As she got swiftly to her feet, tugging at her immaculate gloves, there was the sound of muffled weeping coming from all sides as mothers, wives and sweethearts said their goodbyes to loved ones. Even the band had muted their tone. The Mayoress was handing out packets of sandwiches and cigarettes to the new recruits as they climbed aboard. Eliot got to his feet and picked up his bag, ready to join them.

'You'll send word if you hear anything, about Callum?' He raised his voice against the din of banging doors and the insistent hiss of steam.

She nodded, quite unable to answer. The whistle blasted again and, glancing about, Kate saw that the platform was rapidly emptying with very few soldiers left on it. Most had already boarded, holding the hands of sweethearts through the windows.

'At least you have another child.'

'I do so, and I take good care of her.'

'Are you ever going to tell me if she's mine?'

She saw the bleakness in his eyes, heard the plea in his voice and turned away, unable to bear it. Doors were being banged shut, a porter's whistle, the sound of urgent shouts. 'Ye'd best go.' Still he didn't move a muscle. 'Sure and you'll miss the damn train, if ye don't get a move on.' The last thing she wanted was for him to leave like this. She wanted to hold on to

76

him, to hold back the train, to not let it take him away from her.

Almost as if it were happening in slow motion, she saw how he stiffened his spine, pushed back his shoulders and lift his head in that proud way he had as he glanced back over his shoulder at the waiting train, hissing like a restive animal in its impatience to be off, then he leisurely swung back to her, as if he had all the time in the world, his face unexpectedly soft. 'Will you write to me at least?'

It stunned her momentarily that he should ask, that he should want a letter from her. She could feel her cheeks growing hot at the thought, was perfectly sure her heart was making more noise than the damn band and all the sobbing wives and mothers put together. She very nearly refused, but then remembered his ultimate destination, of how much a letter from home must mean to a soldier. She gave a little shrug, trying to appear indifferent 'Sure and where's the harm in that? I could send the odd postcard, if you like. I might even knit you a balaclava.'

He gave a shout of laughter. 'That's my Kate.' Then before she guessed what he was about, he dropped his bag and swung her up in his arms and the power of his kiss was everything she remembered.

She was still reeling as he snatched up his bag again, managing to leap on to the train just as it began to shunt out of the station. Kate found herself running beside it, waving to him, doing her best to keep sight of his beloved face till the last possible moment, but it wasn't until she reached the end of the platform and had to stop and let it go on without her, that she finally called out, '*Yes*, she is. She's yours.'

–

It was one morning three weeks later that Kate opened the door of her cottage and, to her complete astonishment, found him standing on the doorstep grinning at her. He was in full dress uniform and looked absolutely marvellous.

'I've got forty-eight hours before I leave for France. I've arranged for us to be married at the Parish Church at noon. Can you be ready by then?'

'*What?*'

'Don't argue with me on this, Kate. Don't go into one of your Irish paddies. I don't have time. You know it makes sense. We were meant to be together so stop squabbling with me the whole damned time and do as you're told for once. If nothing else, Flora needs a father.'

'But… but…' She wanted to say but you're going off to war, you've never spoken to Flora, you've never even told me that you love me. Except that her mind was in a whirl and she couldn't seem to get her tongue round the words.

Millie's voice came softly from behind. 'She'll be ready, don't you fret, if I have to carry her there meself.'

Eliot grinned, saluted both women, winked broadly and turning smartly on his heel, strode away, looking every inch the officer.

'I will not!' Kate yelled, the minute the door was slammed shut. 'How can you even imagine that I'd marry that no good, arrogant, full-of-himself bastard who thinks I'm nought but an Irish whore. Jaysus, Mary and Joseph, do you think I'm mad? Why would I do such a damned fool thing?'

Millie was busy riffling through a chest of clothes. 'Because you love the bastard, why else? And think what an exciting forty-eight hours you've got to look forward to. Now, how about this? You always look good in powder blue. Your nightgown is a bit old-fashioned, but I doubt you'll need that anyroad, do you?' She was holding up a crêpe de Chine gown, a wicked smile on her face, a gaggle of children gathered about her, giggling behind their hands.

–

'I can't believe you'd do this to us.' Lucy snapped. Wasn't it enough that she'd been forced to get rid of that dreadful girl's child? Now the little tart had responded by presenting him with another.

Eliot was smiling happily upon his womenfolk, whom he'd deliberately gathered together to impart this latest news, and generously repeated his statement in a clear and steady voice, steadfastly adding more besides. 'I do indeed intend to wed Kate O'Connor. And yes, it's true that we succumbed to

79

a moment of attraction shortly after Amelia's death, when I was grieving and at a low ebb. You mustn't blame her for that. It was my fault entirely. I was out of my mind with grief. Later, for no real reason that I can truly justify, we were intimate again, which has resulted in a beautiful daughter.'

The two maiden aunts blushed furiously and made little clucking noises, not quite knowing where to put themselves.

'Dear God, that doesn't mean you actually have to *wed* the creature,' Lucy spluttered.

'In my eyes it does. Had I known about the child earlier, I would have wed her before the birth, but it is not too late to put matters right. I'm aware it won't be easy for you, nor for the servants, what's left of them, but I hope that you will do your best to welcome her into the family, and give her the support she needs while I'm away fighting in the trenches. Kate has a kind heart and will, I am sure, prove to be a dear sister to you, Lucy.'

'*Sister*? You want the *nursemaid* to be my *dear sister*?'

Eliot rewarded this comment with a flint-hard glare. 'You may recall that she is no longer a servant. Kate has her own business, in which she is doing rather well. I intend to leave Tyson's in her charge, and have no fears that she'll do a good job. So, I hope you weren't going to say something on the lines of 'over my dead body', because none of us would wish you to adopt such an outmoded attitude,

Lucy. These are difficult times and we must pull together. I do mean to go through with this. No one will prevent it.' And he encompassed them all with a warning glance. 'Aunts, I hope you too will welcome my new wife to the fold.'

'Dear me, deary, deary me,' said Cissie, stroking the dog on her lap with such agitation that it woke up and jumped down, yapping excitedly, thinking they were about to play some sort of game. She made a grab for it, trying to calm it.

'What would Amelia say?' said Vera, in shocked tones.

A predictable response but then the aunts had barely tolerated his taking in one innocent child from the stews of Kendal, let alone marrying the mother. 'Amelia would not object.' He raised his voice a notch above the yapping dog. 'She was very fond of Kate, as am I. And she knew how much I wanted children. She wouldn't expect me to ignore this one, particularly not after what happened to Callum.'

'But the child is *illegitimate*.' Words spoken in hushed tones. 'You cannot alter that fact by marrying her.'

'I can try.'

Vera drew herself up into rigid disapproval, spine like an iron rod, her square body seeming to pulsate with shock as she gasped for breath, making little puffing sounds in her throat.

Cissie began to look concerned and giving up on the dog, whom she'd been trying to restrain, put out a consoling hand to pat her sister instead. 'Now don't get into a state, dear.'

Vera said, 'Oh, do hush for once, Cissie, and put that dog out before it drives us all demented. *Marriage*, dear boy is a big step to take. Even I, stickler for propriety as I am, do question the necessity for it. Think of the implications, the position she will be expected to maintain, the access she will have to Tyson money, and this is bound to create one almighty scandal. The gel does not deserve your generosity, she's no better than she should be.'

Eliot laughed. 'A quaint phrase I've never quite understood, but entirely inaccurate. I'm quite certain that we have all misjudged her badly.'

Lucy, who'd been happy for Vera to do most of the hard work, now chipped in to offer support. 'Utter nonsense. If there was ever a case of being trapped into marriage, this is it. Don't let her make a fool of you again, Eliot.'

He walked away to take up his favourite position at the window, hands clasped behind his back as he gazed out upon the smooth dark ribbon of the river, the town he loved so much with its cluster of limestone houses huddled together in this wide, green valley with the distant fells beyond; hoping that in some way the view might calm him. But his patience was fast disintegrating. He'd not expected the breaking of this news to be easy, but he'd be damned if he'd allow them to be quite so obstructive. He certainly had no wish to discuss his feelings on the matter with the women of his family. These were far too personal, and he fully intended to keep them to himself.

At length he turned to face all three of them, his expression as blank as if it were carved in stone, his tone when he addressed them uncompromising, making it clear he would brook no argument, that all discussion on the subject was now at an end. 'The wedding is to take place at noon today. I hope and trust you will all be there to wish me well.' And having made his point, he strode from the room.

Lucy thought she might choke with rage. All her clever planning, all her effort, all those long years of patient waiting, all for *nothing*! Yet she found, to her horror, that she was powerless to prevent it. The wedding did indeed go ahead that very day, in a simple ceremony conducted by the vicar in a fitting and proper manner. The aunts were present, unwillingly making a show of support, but Lucy herself absolutely refused to attend.

She remained in her room in a fury of temper, railing against injustice. When she heard the church bells ring, she snatched up one of her favourite vases and hurled it to the ground. Seeing it smashed into a hundred pieces, she promptly burst into tears.

Oh but she'd have her revenge, she surely would. She wasn't finished, not by a long chalk. If that slut thought she'd won, then she was sadly mistaken.

Chapter Six

Kate was not late, in fact, to her shame, she was early. Fortunately, Eliot was there before her, one of his soldier friends who had volunteered to be best man beside him. All necessary arrangements had been made, a special licence procured, the vicar probably bribed as he smilingly went through the service with brisk efficiency. It surprised her that the aunts were present, looking unnaturally funereal in their customary black, but much to Kate's relief the sour-faced sister-in-law was absent. In fact, no one else attended the simple ceremony except for Millie and, for once, a sober Clem dressed in his best suit, looking as if he'd been scrubbed and buffed to a brilliant shine. Even so, Kate could not claim to be lacking in attendants, either from bridesmaids or pageboys, as the huge church echoed with the chatter and excited giggles of Millie's children and Flora, who all thought it grand fun.

Kate's first concern had been one of alarm, worrying how she was to explain all of this to Flora. 'How on earth do I tell a little girl that this is her daddy who I'm marrying at long last, after all this time. How do I do that, fer God's sake?'

Millie had considered the point with grave seriousness. 'You say, this is yer daddy, pet, and we're getting married at long last.'

Kate gave an exclamation of annoyance, 'Don't make fun of me, Millie. What if she asks why we didn't get married in the first place when she was born? Before she was born, for God's sake, as is the proper way of going about things.'

'You'll say you didn't feel like it at the time, that you hadn't quite made up your mind. She knows how cussed you are, so won't be in the least surprised.'

'But…'

'No more buts Kate, just tell her. Haven't I been saying for years that she has the right to know who her father is?'

And so Kate told her. She went upstairs, sat on her bed and told Flora the whole story, as much of it as seemed appropriate for a five-year-old, desperately striving to ignore the ache in her heart which reminded her she had another child, who would have loved to hear this news. She and Dennis had been round the markets on a number of afternoons during these last few weeks, whatever spare moments she could snatch away from the workshop, which admittedly were few. As soon as this wedding was over, they'd go again. Kate wasn't for giving up on Callum, not while she'd breath in her body.

In the event, Flora took it all on the chin, asking only, 'Can I tell me friend Maggie that I've got a daddy now?'

'Ye can so, sweetheart, because that's what ye'll have.'

'And you're marrying him today, so I get to miss school?'

'I am, and ye do.'

Flora thought about this for a moment. 'I can tell her tomorrow then, can't I? Will I be wearing me best blue frock?'

-

They were standing on Scout Scar, an open fell overlooking the town, having enjoyed a pleasant, if rather quiet, lunch at the Fleece Inn. The aunts would have declined and beat a hasty retreat back to the small parlour, were it not for the fact that Eliot insisted they stay and celebrate his wedding. They'd sat stiff-backed throughout, hardly opening their tightly pressed mouths wide enough to take in a morsel of the excellent Westmorland lamb. Afterwards, Kate and Eliot thanked their guests for coming to share this special day with them, and with Flora skipping along in front of them, the three had walked up Beast Banks, on through Serpentine Woods and out onto the fell. It was a long, steep climb but it was a soft spring day with a bright sun lighting the first primroses, the wayside clotted with wild daffodils and blue pools of bluebells forming a haze of brilliant colour among the long green grasses in the woods.

'They'll never accept me. It's not even worth the trying. Far better if I stay with Millie and Clem while you're away.'

'If you're worrying about the aunts, or Lucy, then don't. I've spoken to them and they are quite resigned, if not exactly jubilant about our decision to marry.'

'Your decision. I don't seem to have had much say in the matter.'

Eliot chuckled. 'Flora seems quite happy with the situation.'

Flora was ecstatic. She'd met her father for the first time outside the great doors of the Parish Church and it was apparent to Kate, to everyone present, that they had liked each other on sight. In typical Flora fashion, she came straight to the point.

'Are you my daddy?'

'I am.'

'And are you going to marry me mammy.'

'If she'll have me.'

'Did you have a quarrel before, that time when I was a babby?'

'I think we must have done.'

'Has Mammy said she's sorry?'

'Not yet. Do you think she might?'

Flora had considered this very seriously for a moment, and then shaken her small head, making the dark curls bounce, the fire in them gleam in the sun. 'Will you say you're sorry to her?'

He gave a rueful smile. 'Sorry enough to ask her to be my wife, will that do?'

A tiny puckering of her brow. 'Mammy says we're to come and live with you.'

'If you approve. I hope you like my house. You'll have a room all to yourself, but you can of course see your friends whenever you wish.' He indicated Millie's children standing close by her side, holding on to her hands and watching the proceedings in wide-eyed wonder.

'Will I be stopping in Mrs Williams's class at school?'

'Oh yes, I should think so. If you want to. Do you like Mrs Williams?'

At this she nodded, and the matter seemed to be settled. Flora released herself from her friends and went to stand before him, gazing up into his face, 'You can kiss me, if you like.'

'Only if you call me Daddy.'

'All right, Daddy. You can kiss me now.'

And he'd swept her up into his arms and smacked a great big raspberry kiss on her cheek, making her squeal with delight.

'So if we've no problems with Flora,' he said now to Kate, watching the little girl in her pretty blue frock hopping and jumping from one tussock of grass to another, 'what else matters? The aunts will come round, once they warm to your charm, as I have done,' he said with a teasing smile. 'Lucy has had the opportunity to express her disapproval but gave up when she saw that it got her absolutely nowhere. So you see, I've made my feelings on the subject very plain.'

That's more than you have to me, Kate thought, but didn't say as much, her eyes on Flora, happily humming a merry little tune to herself.

What had she done on a mad moment of impulse?

Kate was in no doubt over his reasons for marrying her. He wanted Flora. Having lost Callum, he needed a replacement child, particularly now that he was going to war. Perhaps this time he felt it incumbent upon himself to offer her something more substantial than a mere job. Perhaps he realised she would never agree to another adoption, or perhaps he thought it might work out cheaper for him in the end to make her his wife, since she could keep an eye on his business too, for nothing.

And why had she agreed?

Because of Flora? Perhaps she was part of the reason, but much more than that. Because Kate had found herself quite unable to refuse. Even without Millie bullying her every inch of the way to the altar, the thought of being with him, of waking beside him in the morning, of being allowed to care for him, to love him, had been overwhelming, too tempting to refuse.

Kate had thought of him going to France, of possibly losing him for good, and she'd needed some part of him all to herself, in case she did lose him. She'd wanted a glimpse, however momentarily, of how it felt to be his wife.

Of course it had all happened so fast, but these thoughts had raced through her mind. Now, with the knot tied and facing reality, things looked rather different. They were indeed man and wife but Kate couldn't quite come to terms with the fact. How could they ever hope to lead a normal life when the image of Callum still lay between them? What if she never found him? Could she ever hope to banish the guilt of losing him and allow herself to be happy again? When would the agony end? When did time start to heal, as everyone had promised her that it would? The thought that Callum had wandered off and got lost while they were quarrelling; thinking they were angry with each other, angry with him perhaps, haunted her as much today as it ever had, and still brought the occasional nightmare.

Best to turn her mind away from that painful time. Where had agonising ever got her? Concentrate on what was happening now, on the subject in hand. How she was to fit into his life, into Tyson Lodge as his wife. 'What about Amelia's friends? The ladies of Kendal society. Would they ever accept me as your wife? I doubt it.'

'Do you want them to? Do you care whether they do or not?'

'No, of course I don't care, but you can't deny that these people matter.'

'Why should they matter? Do they to you?'

'No, not to me. I don't give two pins for any of them.' Her worries changed to anger now, as they always did, and she turned on him, spitting mad that he couldn't, or wouldn't, understand. 'Jaysus, Mary and Joseph, can't you see it's you they'll hurt, *you* I'm thinking of. There will be the most God-Almighty scandal, just like before. We must have been mad to do this.'

He gave her a sideways glance, a long, narrowed, considering look which seemed to indicate disbelief, as if saying that she should surely be used to scandal, a woman alone with a child. Kate could almost see the thought imprinted in his gaze, almost hear the words on his silent lips.

'Don't look at me like that. I don't care a jot what they say about me, for all I've more morals than you've ever given me credit for, more than them probably. Wasn't I once decently married afore ever I met you?'

He chuckled. 'Are you accusing me of leading you astray?'

'And isn't that the way of it?'

A smile twisted the corner of his mouth, but he said nothing, unnerving her slightly.

'Oh, I don't know what to think. So why did you marry me? Will you tell me that, at least? You could have come to see Flora at any time. I wouldn't have denied you that much, not with the war an' all, and I was even prepared to tell her that you were her daddy.'

'Why do you think I wanted to marry you, Kate?' They'd stopped walking so he could hold her gently in his arms and his voice had grown softer, mesmerisingly so.

She gave a careless shrug. 'How would I know?'

'You can't guess?'

Kate shook her head, deliberately stubborn, pretending not to notice the teasing gleam in his brown eyes.

'Then I'll just have to show you. Not here, of course,' glancing pointedly at the happy child who'd now come to take both their hands, begging them to swing her between them. 'Later, perhaps.'

–

'I'm not sure I'm ready for this.' He was at the far side of the room and, having taken off his jacket and tie, had begun to unbutton his shirt. Kate stood unmoving, filled with a sudden, girlish shyness, knowing she was trembling from head to foot. Between them lay the vast sprawl of a bed and she was perfectly certain that she couldn't go through with it. She simply couldn't. She'd taken one swift, all-encompassing glance, drawn in a deep breath and decided it was best to make her feelings clear right from the start.

At her words, he stopped folding the silk necktie to look across at her in surprise, then as if recognising something vulnerable in her expression, tossed it to one side and came over to take her gently by the shoulders. 'That is entirely your decision, of course. If you prefer to wait, we can. There'll be time enough for – for all of that – later, when I get back.'

'Oh, God, I forgot, you're going away.'

He smiled and shook his head. 'No you hadn't forgotten at all, you just don't care to think about it. Neither do I. I'd like to stay here, with you, for ever. Why did we quarrel, Kate? What was our problem when the attraction between us is so strong?'

'You know well enough, let's not go over all that now. I just want to wait till I'm ready, that's all,' she said crisply, and snatching up her nightdress fled to the bathroom. At least she was allowed to use that now she was no longer a servant.

Later, keenly aware that she was lying in the master's bed, that the aunts were in a room not too far away, perhaps with their nasty little ears pressed to the wall, she lay stiffly beside him. He reached out and touched her hand. Kate instantly turned her back on him, striving to make her breathing sound even and slow, as if she were falling asleep. It didn't seem to be working as he began to stroke her back, his hand moving slowly up and down, easing the tension in her shoulders, melting the stone in her heart so that she could hear her breathing quicken, betraying her need. He seemed to have edged closer as she could feel the warmth from his body searing through her like fire.

'Are you warm enough? Quite comfortable?'

'Yes, thank you.' They were lying side by side in this great bed, yet talking to each other like strangers.

'Does it feel odd sleeping here, in a strange bed? Would you like another pillow, or blanket? Would you, my love?' He was teasing her, she could tell by the lightness in his tone, and it pricked at her conscience that he should be driven to use such tricks on her which, in turn, caused her to flare with fresh annoyance.

'I didn't say I was cold, I said I was tired.' She thumped her pillow and tried to move away from him as far as the bed would allow but he laid an arm about her waist, capturing her again, and Kate felt certain he would feel her heart beating.

He stroked the back of her wrist with his thumb and, sensing the weakening effect his caresses were having on her, she flounced up in the bed, masking her trembling with a coating of anger. 'How will I ever get to sleep if you're interfering with me the whole time.'

To her utter amazement he burst out laughing, lay back against the cool sheets and roared till even Kate found the corners of her lips twitching.

'What? What is it? What have I said?'

'I thought a husband was supposed to *interfere* with his wife on their wedding night, particularly if she is as lovely as you.'

She could see the gleam of his eyes reflected in a shaft of moonlight, the whiteness of his teeth in the semi-darkness, and something inside her began to melt. 'Is that what I am? Your lovely wife? You think I'm lovely, or are you making fun of me again?'

He reached up and stroked the glorious tumble of red hair, smoothing his hand over her soft cheek, along the line of her throat, sliding the thin night-gown from one naked shoulder and making her shudder with longing.

'I swear you are the loveliest creature I ever set eyes on. I always thought so. Why, in God's name, we've spent so much of these last years at odds, I cannot comprehend. I shall carry the image of how you look this night with me forever. Will you write to me every single day, my love? Will you remember me with perhaps just a little affection when I'm out there in the mud of the trenches?'

She was lost. Kate felt a great lump of emotion rise in her throat, could barely breathe, let alone speak. 'Oh Eliot, course I will. Don't you know that I love the bones of ye. I always have. I'll love you to till the day I die. Why else would I have agreed to this madness?'

Eliot felt his stomach tighten in that all too familiar way, yet still he managed to maintain his control. One wrong move now and he could lose her for ever. He gave a rueful smile, cupping her cheek with a soothing hand. 'Will you stop being angry with me then, at least long enough to kiss me,' and this time when he pulled her gently into his arms, she came willingly.

–

When they woke the next morning Kate put out a hand and instinctively reached for him. Amazingly, he was still there. It hadn't been a dream but magical reality. She rolled over to straddle him, kissing him awake. 'Wake up, are you tired of me already?'

'Never!'

She nibbled at his ear, licked the erotic curve of it, rubbed her lips enticingly against his, angling her body so that he could enjoy the soft fullness of her breasts. 'I think perhaps ye don't have the stamina to keep up with me.'

'Minx, I'll show you who has stamina,' and grabbing her around the waist, he pulled her beneath him and began to make love to her all over again.

Out on the landing, as the aunts bustled down to the dining room, they heard the squeals and made small clucking noises with their tongues. 'I really can't think what came over him to behave in such a dreadful, devil-may-care fashion. He'll rue the day,' Aunt Vera said, in her sourest tones. 'Rue the day.'

'Oh, indeed, you are absolutely correct, sister. They will both regret this marriage,' Cissie agreed, and, calling to the two pointers to stop snuffling at the bedroom door, the two maiden ladies made their way down to breakfast; spines rigid, heads held high, deliberately deaf to the noises emanating from behind the closed door.

In the nursery, Flora was already regretting her mother's hasty marriage. Yesterday had been so exciting, what with the new blue frock, the thrill of the wedding, and getting a new daddy. Now, Aunt Lucy was standing by her bed, ordering her to get up in a very nasty, bossy voice. 'You're a naughty girl to be still lying in bed. You should have been down to breakfast fifteen minutes ago. Don't you understand that it's rude to be late for meals? You aren't even dressed.'

'Mammy helps me dress.'

'A big girl like you? What nonsense! Anyway, your mammy isn't interested in you any more, not now that she's got a new husband.'

'She is. My mammy loves me.'

'Not any more.' Lucy whipped back the sheets and eiderdown and Flora instinctively curled up into a tiny ball and closed her eyes, hoping the nasty lady wouldn't be able to see her any more, or that when she opened her eyes again, she would have vanished in a puff of smoke.

'Get out of bed this minute and wash and dress yourself before I take my slipper to you. Don't expect any help from your mammy. She's too busy to spend any time with you now, so you must do as *I* tell you. This is *my* house. *I'm* in charge here, not your *mammy*! Come along now, stop shivering, get that nightie off.'

Flora struggled out of bed and obediently began to pull off her nightgown, small tears forming at the corners of her eyes, although she was desperately trying not to let them fall. She quickly pulled on her drawers and her vest with the little sleeves, but then got confused as she tried to tie the ribbons on her petticoat. She could do a knot on her shoelaces, like Miss Williams had shown her, but didn't always get the bow quite right. Her small fingers went round and round with the loop, in and out, but somehow it wouldn't stay in place. It kept coming undone and now she could hardly see what she was doing, for the tears in her eyes had grown too big to see through them properly.

'Get on with it child, we haven't all day.'

'I c–can't…'

'There's no such word as can't, and don't answer back. You are a very stupid girl. Put your hands on your head. *Now!*'

Flora jerked as if she'd been struck.

'Do it *now!*'

In an instinctive bid to protect herself, the child obeyed. She clasped her hands on top of her head and her lips started to tremble. Even though she pressed them together very hard, the bottom one still wobbled.

'Don't you dare move an inch,' Lucy warned, grabbing her by the shoulders and giving her a little shake, 'or there will be a worse punishment for you. You shall miss breakfast this morning because you've been so lazy. But if you're a good girl and do as I say from now on, then I won't tell your mammy how naughty you've been. Do you understand?'

Wide-eyed, the frightened little girl pressed down even harder on her wobbling lip and dutifully nodded.

Chapter Seven

The workers at the factory found it hard to accept her. Simply being Eliot's wife wasn't enough, since the working man's view of women was pitifully low. Wives, in their opinion, had a limited value, a role which should be confined either to minding the children and keeping house, or in the bedroom. Certainly not on the factory floor. Nor were they interested in the fact that Kate had made her mark in the shoe industry with her own workshop, which was smaller and entirely different. And it had produced only boots for the army. She knew nothing about making classic lines, the quality shoes for which Tyson's was famous.

And of course far too many of them, Swainson included, remembered her as a simple nursemaid. Without exception they thought she'd got above herself.

'Who does she think she is?' they would mutter whenever she issued an order, encouraged to react in this way by Swainson himself.

Kate had expected trouble from the foreman, and she got it. She was aware of these rumblings of discontent, knew the men were deliberately working to rule and not pulling together. One by one they would come to her and complain that a consignment of shoes, or boots, could not possibly be produced in the time she'd allowed; that some order or other had been 'accidentally' overlooked; that the leather was faulty; a machine had broken down; any and every excuse under the sun. She tried talking to them, man to man as it were, appealing to their better natures, their patriotic spirit, but got absolutely nowhere.

'Come on lads,' she would say, 'there's a war on. You can do better than this. Jump to it.' But they didn't jump to it. They didn't put themselves out in the slightest. And all the while she was aware of Swainson smirking in the background.

She'd left Toby Lynch, her trusty foreman, in charge of her own workshop at the old ropeworks, and with gritted teeth told herself she'd just have to learn to work with Swainson here at the factory. Eliot had warned her not to expect too much, that they were behind him for some reason, and would have no compunction about walking out and destroying the business completely if she did anything hasty they disagreed with, such as sack him. So she held her patience. For now.

-

Early in the new year, Kate found that she had a serious shortage of men. With a fall off of volunteers, the government were bringing in conscription. It was not a popular move and many men objected, but the decision was irrevocable. The war must be brought to a satisfactory conclusion and with all speed. Even Dennis, along with many of her most skilled operatives, had been called up. Kate thought, for a time, that she might be about to lose Toby, but managed to get him excused on the grounds of his being in charge of the production of boots for soldiers.

Finding herself in dire straits, she put an advertisement in the local *Westmorland Gazette*, offering training to any women willing to take their place. She got a surprisingly good response with more than enough women ready to take on the challenge. Patriotism was running high.

Kate took them on and resolved to make some changes. She made adjustments to the shift patterns to allow those women who wished to, to work nights along with the men, so they could be with their families for at least a part of each day. All hell broke loose. The older men strongly objected, resenting the idea of the factory being invaded by a bunch of women, and a strike was called in protest. Each day the men would gather at the factory gates, waving their placards and shouting offensive remarks to anyone brave enough to breach the picket line. Many women stopped trying, refusing to go in to work because they were too afraid. But there were others who valiantly turned up each and every morning, determined to get in somehow. Sally

Wilshaw was such a one, showing her resourcefulness by climbing in through a lavatory window, until one of the men spotted her and bolted it from the inside.

'They'll not stop me,' she cried, gritting her teeth and rolling up her sleeves in a burst of fighting spirit that would have gone down well on the Somme.

One morning, as Sally and her two best mates, Joan Enderby and Nell Benson, marched boldly up to the gates, things suddenly turned nasty. The three women were jostled by a group of angry-looking men who very swiftly surrounded them. 'Hey up, you lot,' Sally yelled at them. 'Bugger off. We've a right to go to work, same as you lot. We allus have worked harder than you, you daft lump.'

'Not in our factory, you haven't. Go back to yer bloody kitchen. We don't want no women here, taking work away from men.'

'Don't talk daft. There's no men round 'ere, they're all off fighting in t'war, where you should be, Bill Grigson.' Suddenly becoming aware of other men drawing close behind her, Sally swung round to face them, fists clenched, ready to punch any who dared touch her. 'Here, what the 'ell,' but she got no further as a stone was thrown. It hit her on the back of her head and knocked her out cold. Nell and Joan ran to help but the men refused to let the women through, jeering and yelling, pushing and shoving them back and forth like rubber balls between them, till the women were sobbing with fear.

A voice rang out above the din. 'Holy Mother, what do you lot think ye're doing with my workers? Get yer hands off them, Jack Milburn, if'n ye know what's good for ye.'

A hush fell in the factory yard as all eyes turned towards her. Kate was a fearsome figure to behold as she stood, hands on hips, the blazing oriole of hair around her head matched only by the fire in her smoke-grey eyes. 'Isn't your son at the Front, Will Barker? And yours too, Tom Perry, and yours Joe? So you can all take that menacing look off yer daft faces and get back to work afore I sack the lot of you.'

Jack Milburn, ever the troublemaker, took a step forward, not a sign of softening in the cold hard lines of his face. 'My son will be back when the war ends, probably by next Christmas, and then where will he be, with no job to come back to? Out on the streets, that's where.'

'There'll be work for him right enough, don't you fret, whenever he comes home. And you know as well as I do that this war won't be over by Christmas. In the meantime, we have boots to make, if'n your lad isn't to fight the Hun barefoot, so get back to your machines, the lot of you.'

Kate thought for a moment that they were going to obey her and go quietly back to work, albeit grumbling under their breath, but then a familiar figure emerged from the shadow of a doorway.

Swainson. Dear Lord, she should have guessed he'd be behind this.

He stood before her, attempting to intimidate her into submission by his very presence. 'I'll thank you to get out of my yard. If you've anything to say to my men, you can address them through me.'

'Is that so?' Kate wasn't in the least intimidated by the man, only angry he dared to stand against her.

'It is. They do what I tell 'em.'

'So what gives you the right of life and death over their souls, because that's what yer saying. If they don't work, they don't get paid, and if they don't get paid, they starve. In the meantime, their sons die on the field of battle, presumably in their bare feet.'

There was a small, telling silence. All eyes turned to look at Swainson, his wandering eye lurching sideways, lip curled into a snarl. 'We working men are used to fighting exploitation by the ruling classes, and from them jumped-up 'uns who are pretending to be what they're not.'

A collective in-drawing of breath, for no matter what anyone might say about the rights and wrongs of employing women, this was the boss's wife he was insulting here, a woman who'd made quite a name for herself in the town. Kate simply smiled, as if he'd said something to amuse her. 'Exploitation? Is that you call it? And there's me thinking we were fighting a war, not each other. I thought it was the Hun who was our enemy, and we were working nicely together, as a team: all British, all Kendalians, all proud to be doing our bit. But then, what do I know? I'm just a daft woman.

'Seems to me like you're the one always giving orders round here, not me at all,' she continued, in a calm voice. 'Why is that, I wonder? Pissed off, are you, because you can't get your grubby little hands on my women any more? Is that it? Do these men know how many of their wives you've been poking while they pay you to be their spokesman? I bet they don't.'

The silence in the yard now was oppressive and Kate wondered if she'd gone too far. She still had no proof to back up these allegations. Not one of the women had ever been brave enough to speak up and complain, neither to Eliot, nor to their husbands. It had all been hushed up, swept under the carpet as something unclean and best not investigated too closely. Why should she imagine they'd be any different now? But she'd reckoned without Sally.

'Aye, she's right.' Her voice sounded cracked and raw with pain, a mere echo of its former resonance but there wasn't a man present didn't hear every word. 'He certainly did his worst wi' me, filthy bugger.'

There was an achingly long silence, and then a second voice. 'And me,' echoed Joan Enderby, stepping forward.

'Me an' all,' added Nell Benson.

Thus encouraged by this show of bravery, other women stepped forward, coming to stand beside these three, silently offering their support; the blazing defiance in their steady gazes challenging anyone to doubt that they'd been anything but unwilling victims in Swainson's climb to power.

They turned on Swainson as one man and the fear in his ferrety face was palpable. He was driven from that yard by a shouting, rowdy, dangerous crowd of angry men, Jack Milburn, Bill Grigson and Tom Perry along with him. All Kate did was stand by and silently watch, grinning from ear to ear.

–

Matters improved considerably after that, at least in the factory. At home was another matter. Lucy continued to treat Kate as some sort of glorified servant, if not exactly a nursemaid since there was only Flora to see to. In her opinion, it was most useful to have someone to call upon to do her bidding.

'Kate, will you just bring my wrap from my bedroom,' she would say, without glancing up from her magazine or her crochet work. Or, 'Do ask Mrs Petty if we can have tea early today, and some of her delicious cream buns.' At first, anxious to fit in and be accepted, Kate would obey, until it came to her one day that she was doing all the running about in the household, all the fetching and carrying, even to lighting fires and filling coal scuttles, particularly since Fanny was no longer there to do any of these tasks, and poor Ida could scarcely cope with all the extra duties. But hadn't she enough to do, running the factory? Surely if she could deal with that nasty piece of shite, Swainson, who'd never set foot in the works since that stand-off in the yard, she could sort out one snobby sister-in-law.

The next time Lucy asked her to fetch something, a handkerchief this time which she could quite easily fetch herself, Kate politely declined. 'Sorry Lucy, but I'm just working on these balance sheets, and might lose my concentration if I break off.'

Lucy was shocked by this lack of deference. 'I beg your pardon? I've just asked you to do a job for me. Are you refusing?'

'Well, would you believe it, so I am. It may have slipped your notice but I'm no longer employed as a servant in this house. We don't in fact have a housemaid any more. Fanny has left.'

'Gone to work for you in that dreadful little workshop, I understand.'

Kate beamed cheerfully. 'My "dreadful little workshop" as you call it, is now part and parcel of Tyson Industries, so you'd best get used to the idea. But yes, that is where Fanny is happily ensconced. And although I've tried placing several advertisements in the local press, I've found no replacement housemaid, so we are all going to have to pull our weight a little bit more than usual. At least until hostilities are over and things settle back to normal.'

'Well, really! You surely aren't expecting me to sweep and clean? Isn't it enough that I've sacrificed my lady's maid because of Eliot's parsimony? These Tyson brothers were always mean, dreadfully so, considering their vast wealth.'

Kate sighed and sorrowfully shook her head. 'And isn't that what I thought meself once? They appeared wealthy, certainly from Poor House Lane, but now I'm not so sure. This is a big house to run, the aunts, and you, live in it and need to be kept, along with your children and their school fees paid. Eliot does his duty, bless his generous heart, but the money has to be found from somewhere. And there are God knows how many other aunts and uncles and cousins who depend upon Tyson's to furnish them with pensions or dividends on their shares. You, *dear sister-in-law*, are not the only one making demands upon him. Perhaps you should remember that occasionally.'

Lucy bridled at being reminded of their relationship. Had she been a cat, her fur would have stood on end and her claws unsheathed. 'Is that meant as some sort of criticism?'

'No,' Kate replied calmly. 'It's meant as a comment on the facts. Eliot carries all the responsibility for this family on his broad shoulders, which mebbe you should appreciate a bit more. I'm surprised ye've made no progress finding yerself a new chap. Course, it isn't easy nowadays, not with all the best men going off to war, and there'll be even fewer when it's over, I shouldn't wonder. So if you couldn't find a husband before, I doubt you'll have much better luck after.' She gave a sad shake of her head. 'What a waste. I'm sorry for your misfortune, so I am.'

Lucy's cheeks fired to scarlet, and she leapt to her feet in a fury. 'I'm not asking for your pity.'

'No, course you aren't,' Kate continued, at her most pleasant. 'Only to fetch ye a handkerchief, or whatever it is ye've a fancy for next. But we can't find a maid, do ye see, let alone a rich husband. And I'm sorry I can't help like I used to, but since Eliot has left the responsibility for Tyson Industries in my hands, and the workers depend upon it for their livelihoods, not to mention all the rest of the Tyson family, the factory must have first call upon my time. I hope you understand. We must all do our best to pull together and get along, eh?'

Words which were echoed in Eliot's own letters home from the front. 'I hope you and Kate are getting along better now,' he would say.

And Lucy would write back. 'We are like dear sisters.'

Kate found that once she'd made it clear that she was no longer a servant but Eliot's wife, and should be treated as such, she coped quite well with her new role. Her fears for Eliot increased over the long months of his absence. At the end of last year he'd been involved in the fracas over Gallipoli, an ill-conceived campaign which Kitchener had finally abandoned when he'd gone out there to inspect the situation at first hand. She'd spent a tense few weeks before hearing that Eliot had been safely evacuated along with his men.

She'd received several letters after that, a whole bunch of them which gave her a small insight into the horrors he was facing, although some words had been scored through by the censor. Eliot spoke of the horrors of the trenches, the slush and mud, the stink and blood of dying men, how there'd been times when they were sick with fear or fed up to the back teeth; his pain over losing one of his men, as well as his fury if one wasn't pulling his weight.

'They are so young, Kate. Little more than boys. Some of them can't even…' and again obliteration of his words by the censor, but Kate assumed them to be, 'fire a rifle.'

Sometimes he spoke of his need for her. Nothing overly romantic, just a few plain, simple words scribbled on the bottom. 'I miss you, Kate,' or 'Thinking of you, my love.'

She thought of him too, every day. And when the pain and worry became too great, she would bury her fears in work, as she always did.

–

In July, the British launched their offensive on the Somme although even that grand military campaign was soon bogged down in controversy. Despite its apparently careful planning, losses were huge and soon Rolls of Honour were being posted in the parish church. Kate became obsessed with calling in, just to make sure Eliot's name wasn't on it and someone had forgotten to inform her. Shrines to the fallen appeared everywhere, at churches up and down the land, on street corners, outside ordinary houses in the streets of Kendal, all with names and flowers, prayers or crosses set beside them.

Kate helped her women workers make up parcels of cigarettes and Kendal mint cake, socks and even the balaclavas she'd once flippantly promised Eliot, to send out to the soldiers. When once he wrote to say that nothing was getting through, she contacted several food suppliers in town, who agreed to send out parcels to the soldiers, all packed together in a great big van, which did get through and was gratefully received.

But as the summer wore on, his letters became less frequent, their contents more guarded, which caused her to worry all the more.

She did at least get a letter from Dermot saying that as conscription didn't apply to Irishmen, he'd not been forced to go. He was doing well with his own little business, he told her.

> Though not as well as yours, mind. Aren't you the grand one now? Me and Dolly have three babbies, and still happy as Larry after nearly six years of marriage. I'd come and see you, Katy love, only we never have two halfpennies to rub together. One day, eh me lovely? Keep those Irish eyes smiling.

Kate shed many a tear over that letter, reading and re-reading it over and over till she knew every word by heart. Wouldn't she just love to see her little brother again? Aw, but you couldn't have everything in this world, and he was fine and dandy, safe enough where he was. There were many who weren't so lucky. Too many. Fear and anxiety for their loved ones ran through everyone these days, though it was true she'd little enough family that she could afford to lose sight of any one of hers. She'd never found the red-haired boy Flora had spoken of, had lost heart that she ever would. It had probably not been Callum anyway. Kate decided that he was simply a figment of the child's imagination. But that wouldn't stop her search continuing. Only right now, she'd little enough time, not with a factory and a work-shop to run.

There were times when she suffered pangs of conscience over leaving Flora more and more in the care of the two aunts, and with Lucy. But then Cissie was quite fond of the child and would happily read her stories for hours, much to Flora's delight. Vera, on the other hand, would read only carefully selected stories from the bible. Fortunately, Flora liked these too, which softened even Aunt Vera's stony heart, at least a little. It seemed to Kate at times, that her daughter was making better progress with them than she was. She even got on well with Cissie's hysterical dogs.

But if they had learned to tolerate the child, the maiden aunts rarely spoke to Kate, except to issue her with an order or instruction of some sort, which she generally ignored. Or else it would be to chide her on some supposed failing. 'Eliot would wish you to leave the letters on the tray in the hall, not take them to the post office yourself.'

'But who else will take them, if not me? Fanny works at the factory now. Dennis has enlisted. Dear old Askew is no longer with us, and Mrs Petty and Ida have enough to do. Who else would post the letters, will ye tell me that? Your good selves, mebbe?'

But she never won an argument. They would find some other fault instead. 'Poor dear Amelia always used to have the brasses polished on a Friday. These are looking very grubby dear. Quite dilapidated.'

'Then here's a rag, give them a rub, why don't you? Or ask Lucy. She's not got much on this week.'

'Well, I never!'

'Oh, deary, deary me.'

They still hadn't quite accepted her for what she was, a vital part of Eliot's life. Winning the men over had been easy by comparison.

Chapter Eight

Lucy wasted no time in taking advantage of Kate's distraction. The fact that running the factory was taking all her attention was proving to be a positive bonus. It had the wonderful benefit of allowing Lucy long periods alone with the child, and she willingly volunteered to collect Flora from school.

'You see how I have taken your words to heart about us all pulling together. This is my way of doing my bit, *dear* sister. One way, at least, that I can help, and with my own children away at school, it is a pleasure to spend time with a child again.'

And the joy of it was, Kate believed her. She would kiss her sleepy daughter while she was still in her bed, and dash off without a second thought, completely trusting.

Lucy was beginning to really quite enjoy herself, growing more imaginative in her abuse of this child which had been foisted upon the household. Not only did the luckless Flora stand in very well as a make-shift servant to fetch and carry her knitting wool, embroidery threads, books or whatever, but from that very first morning when Lucy had made the situation clear, the child had proved to be a surprisingly quick learner.

Dear Flora had a natural instinct for survival which meant she responded well to the fear Lucy induced in her, and proved to be surprisingly easy to control. Disappointingly easy at times, which meant that Lucy needed to devise new trials to provoke her, if she was to remain entertained and not grow bored by the whole enterprise.

It was such a marvellous way of relieving her own personal frustration and fury. So utterly satisfying to take out her revenge on the child.

She would order Flora to stand in a corner for lengthy periods with her hands on her head whenever she didn't instantly obey one of Lucy's instructions to the letter, or else pinch the flesh on her tummy or on the backs of her legs, somewhere any unfortunate marks were less likely to show. By way of variation, Lucy would put a blanket over the child's head while she slapped her quite hard, to and fro with the flat of her hand. That way there would be no bruises. At first, Flora had cried a great deal during these ordeals, but the little girl soon learned that this only resulted in yet worse punishment and would now suck in her breath, bite her lip and keep silent, which, oddly enough, infuriated Lucy all the more. It seemed to issue a further challenge, and she'd be desperate to find some way to make the child cry.

'I'll break your stubborn spirit, drat you,' she would hiss through gritted teeth. 'You are so *very* naughty, no wonder your mammy neglects you and doesn't love you any more. You are going to have to learn better manners, or nobody will love you ever again.'

'Yes she does love me,' Flora stubbornly insisted, pouting her wobbly lips, and be slapped even harder for this show of defiance.

Sometimes, if Lucy should offer to take her for a walk to feed the ducks or up to Serpentine Woods, Flora would object, becoming tearful over this promised treat.

'No, I want Mammy. Mammy, you take me for a walk.' And she would cling to her mother's skirt, or drag her feet and refuse to go.

Kate would panic, worried that Flora wasn't finding it any easier than herself to settle into this new routine with a strange family in a strange home. She would hold her close and soothe her, trying to reassure her precious child. 'There now, won't ye have a grand time? You must thank Aunt Lucy for offering to look after you so well when Mammy's busy.'

'But I want *you* to look after me. You never do. You don't love me no more.'

'Now where did you get that nonsense from?'

'Aunt Lucy said you don't, not if I'm naughty.' A gulp and a guilty swallow, since this was dangerous territory.

'I'm sure she didn't say anything of the sort. Wouldn't she only be telling you to be a good girl so's yer mammy would be proud of ye. And sure I am proud of ye. Don't I love the bones of you? Aren't you my precious treasure?' And Kate hugged her daughter tight, to prove it. 'I know it's hard for you to understand, sweetheart, but there's a war on, and our brave soldiers have gone out to fight to protect us all. Daddy has left Mammy in charge of the factory. That's my war job, d'you see? Not only do I have boots to make for all these fine soldiers but I must see that the business is run properly, that all the workers are properly looked after, orders taken and dealt with so the factory will still be here for Daddy when he comes home again at the end of it all. Do you understand, me cushla?'

Even as Kate patiently offered this explanation as simply and clearly as she could, half of her mind was worrying over what fresh trouble might be brewing, whether a promised order had been completed, if she could squeeze a free day to go off round the markets again on yet another fruitless search for Callum. And also worrying over when she'd last had a letter from Eliot, not for two weeks surely? So much to think about, so many worries.

'Mammy wants you to be a brave little soldier too, d'you see?' Kate said, unconsciously worsening the situation.

For Flora it was all very confusing. She understood about the war, and her mammy working hard, but she still couldn't get rid of that nasty feeling in her tummy. Something wasn't right and it must be her fault because hadn't they all had that lovely wedding, hadn't she worn her best dress, acquired a new daddy and come to live in this great big house? Even her friend Maggie had been impressed. So she should be happy, shouldn't she? And if nobody liked her, and kept smacking her, it must be her fault, mustn't it? Oh, why was everything so muddled? And why couldn't she make Aunt Lucy pleased with her?

The battles over the meals were, to Lucy, a particular delight. She just loved breakfast times. Flora hated eggs. It didn't matter whether they were boiled, fried, scrambled, any way Mrs Petty chose to make them, she absolutely refused to eat eggs. Kate said that she'd always disliked them.

'You're too soft with that child. Always were, and with Callum too.'

'Callum isn't here now, so let's not bring him into this,' Kate firmly insisted, and Lucy gave a careless shrug.

Mrs Petty offered various alternatives. 'If the little petal doesn't care for eggs, would she like a nice fat sausage for her breakfast instead? Or a bit of crispy bacon?'

'I'm sure that would be lovely,' Lucy agreed, thrilled to have found a new and imaginative way to plague the child. 'But I'll take the eggs, Mrs Petty. You know how I do love them.'

The aunts always ate their own breakfast early at seven, so Lucy made a point of waiting until they'd finished before taking Flora in. Then she put the specially prepared sausage on to her own plate and gave the two poached eggs to the child. Flora turned up her nose in disgust.

'Don't want them. Don't *like* eggs, Aunt Lucy.'

'You'll eat what's good for you, like them or not.' And when it became clear, as anticipated, that she was not going to eat them, Lucy began spooning great lumps of the rapidly congealing mess into the child's protesting mouth. Flora began spitting and crying in most satisfactory distress.

The following morning was even better. Lucy stood behind the child's chair, arms folded, and took immense pleasure in watching how she struggled to eat the hated egg through choking tears, gagging over the yolk which she loathed most of all.

'You really need far more discipline. Your mammy has spoilt you, but *I'm* in charge now, so you'll do as *I* say.'

Lucy had another brilliant idea. If drilling was good for soldiers, she thought, why not for a small child? She conducted these 'exercises', as she liked to call them, out on Scout Scar, far away from the house and any prying eyes, where she could be in complete control. She insisted Flora march back and forth over a given area, arms either raised above her head, or constantly swinging, for hour upon hour. This became a regular routine, often in the pouring rain, till the child was weeping and giddy with exhaustion. Lucy would generously allow her a short respite before brutally making her start all over again.

'Fifty times. You must walk this path fifty times without stopping. Your daddy drills because of the war, so why not you? Do it right, and I'll tell him what a good little soldier you are.'

There was the odd awkward moment. Should they return home with the child soaking wet, Lucy would hurry her upstairs through the silent house before anyone could see, handing her a towel with the order to strip off and dry herself.

To Flora's credit, she made less and less fuss, withdrawing into a silent shell which she cast about herself, as if she'd grown indifferent to pain and punishment. As a consequence, she did indeed become more disciplined, a great deal better behaved, both at mealtimes and in company.

Kate would remark upon it, saying what a 'good girl' she was, thus seeming to condone the situation in Flora's eyes. Other days, she would look slightly troubled, saying how quiet Flora had been at bedtime, asking if she was sickening for something.

Lucy always dismissed such a notion as utter nonsense. 'She's tired out from playing so hard all day, that's all. You really mustn't fuss the child, sister dear.'

Even Vera would put on her spectacles and frowningly comment, 'We don't like noise here. Children should be seen and not heard.'

Flora's increasing reserve, so far as Lucy was concerned, only proved that the 'exercises' were working. The purpose, after all, was to 'instil discipline' and if the result caused Kate O'Connor some concern, all well and good. A little bit of worry was excellent, exactly what that little whore deserved, so long as it didn't get out of hand so that she realised what was really going on.

–

Callum had never entirely forgotten his past but it remained somewhat distant and unreal; a muddle of half dreams, half memory. Now he had another puzzle to add to it. The day he'd met that girl at Kendal market stood out in his mind like a beacon. Not simply because she'd generously given him half her sweet, which had been pretty much all he'd had to eat that day, bar one apple and a lump of hard cheese, but because he'd caught a glimpse of her lovely mother. For some strange reason he couldn't explain, she'd looked familiar.

Ever since that day, he'd kept a lookout, longed to see her again. He never had, sadly. They rarely went to Kendal, it being a long way from the farm, and Mrs Brocklebank didn't always let him go with her to the local markets at Keswick and Ambleside, more often leaving him with a list of chores to keep him busy on the farm while she was away. Now that he'd grown bigger, his workload had increased considerably.

'Great lad like you needs to pull yer weight, since you eat so much,' Mr Brocklebank would say. 'About time you were some use round 'ere.' As if he'd never done a hand's turn in all these long years.

'Nay, he's a growing lad, aren't you, Allan?' Mrs Brocklebank might add, if she was feeling kindly towards him.

If she did take him with her, he'd be kept working the whole time so he was never able to wander off and do any exploring on his own account. Mrs Brocklebank didn't allow any show of independence.

But now he was thirteen and a half and not quite so biddable, and he'd grown big enough not to be cowed by her bully of a husband. In his bed in the dusty, cold barn, Callum would work on his plan of escape night after night. He was haunted by the vision of that woman: her lovely face, the red hair so like his own, those brilliant, clear grey eyes. She'd stood only yards away from him, calling to the girl, so he'd had several moments in which to study her. It had felt almost as if time were standing still in that instant. And then she'd smiled at the child, hugged her close as if she were precious, gently scolded her for wandering off and then hurried her away, not even noticing himself standing there watching.

And if, at the back of his mind, he wondered if she was the one, if this lovely woman could possibly be the mother he'd been dreaming of all these years, he didn't dare to let the thought grow. But then one of the other stallholders told him once that someone had been asking after him. He'd hoped it was she, but then he'd put that notion from his mind too. He knew that hope was a dangerous thing.

But the possibility that she just might be looking for him had never gone away. The idea that she might indeed be his mother intrigued and excited him. Somehow he had to find her, and ask.

Today was May Day, 1917, and as luck would have it they were once again off to Kendal to the butter market. Mr Brocklebank hadn't been available to drive the cart, so that task had fallen to him. As usual, he helped the farmer's wife set up the stall and arrange their wares. The morning was busy with shoppers, as always, but all the time he was looking for an opportunity to slip away, to put his carefully laid plan into effect. His chance came early in the afternoon when Mrs Brocklebank began gossiping with the woman on the next stall. Normally, he would have taken the opportunity to have a bit of a rest on the edge of the cart, if no one was wanting butter and eggs, but this was the best chance he'd get to look for the red-haired woman, perhaps his only one, and he meant to take it.

With her back turned, Mrs Brocklebank didn't see him slip under the stall and crawl away. When

Callum believed himself to be out of sight, he got to his feet and ran hell for leather. Hopefully, she wouldn't spot that he was missing until he was several streets away. What would happen later, when he returned, he didn't care to think about too closely. Best just run for it, even if he hadn't a clue where, exactly, he was running to, or where he might find the woman.

He ran helter-skelter down Branthwaite Brow, his boots clattering on the cobbles, and instinctively turned left when he reached Finkle Street, not pausing until he'd run the length of Stramongate and reached the bridge where he skittered to a halt and stared in astonishment at the river.

A prickle of recognition made the hair at the back of his neck rise. *He'd been here before! He knew this place!* But how and why? So far as he could recall, he'd only ever been to Kendal market a couple of times before with Mrs Brocklebank, and never once been permitted to wander anywhere on his own. When they drove into town on the farmer's cart, they always came down Windermere Road. He didn't remember them ever crossing the river at this point, over this particular bridge. Or could he be wrong about that? Had he travelled this way as a boy with the Brocklebanks on some occasion or other? Was he simply confused?

He had a sudden vision of a woman in a smart grey coat and a big hat with a feather. She was holding his hand, shaking him quite hard and shouting at him. He was crying, because he was frightened. Who was this woman, and why was she so angry? Callum knew, with absolute conviction, that it wasn't Mrs Brocklebank. Nor was this the woman whose face had haunted his dreams throughout his boyhood. This was a new memory. Someone else entirely.

His feet were taking him on over the bridge, past a church which made him shiver with foreboding for some reason, then out on to a broad sward of grass.

'What's this place called?' he asked a boy passing by on his bicycle.

'Gooseholme. Where you looking for? Have you to deliver summat to Thorny Hills?'

Thorny Hills. The name hummed in his head like a familiar tune. He'd definitely heard the name before. He *had* been here before. He knew it. He *knew* it!

His excitement was growing but he let his feet make the decisions about which way to go. They led him unerringly across the grass, out through a lych-gate and stopped by the walls of a big, square, grey-stoned house. He drew in a deep breath, unlatched the garden gate and walked up the path.

At the door he spit on his hands and rubbed them over his face, did the same again, this time flattening down his unruly copper curls, tucked his cap tidily away in his pocket. He could do nothing about the none-too-clean working shirt and fustian trousers, the braces and mucky clogs, so he stretched up and tugged on the bell pull. He heard the sound of it echo deep in the belly of the house, and again there was that prickling sensation that he'd done this before, heard that sound before. Nothing happened. There was no response, no answer and he tugged on the bell pull again.

Callum found he was holding his breath so much that it hurt, and he let it out on a gasp. He'd almost given up hope, had half turned away, deciding nobody could be in after all, when the door was pulled open. He swung about, his young face bright and eager for this first meeting with the woman he'd dreamed of for so long. Would she be the one? Was this the moment he would at last meet his mother?

Chapter Nine

'Was that the bell?' Mrs Petty held the buttered scone poised in one hand, a knife loaded with jam in the other while she put her head to one side to listen. 'Did you hear anything, Ida?'

Ida sniffed, rubbing the back of her hand across her nose to wipe the drip from it. Of course she'd heard the bell, but she'd no wish to leave this warm fire, or this lovely tea Mrs Petty had done for them because Fanny was paying one of her customary visits. Nor had she any wish to miss the ending of one of Fanny's stories, which were always titillating. 'No, Mrs P, I didn't hear nuffin'.' Let madam answer. She'd nothing else to do all day. Ida was taking an hour off.

'You'd best go and check. Get along with you then. Don't sit there looking gormless.'

With reluctance, Ida set down her plate, casting a lingering glance back at her scone as she scuttled quickly out into the hall. She could see a boy at the door. He had copper-coloured hair and a bright smile on his face, though even as Ida watched, the smile quickly faded as he looked up into madam's face. Not that this surprised her. Madam Lucy wasn't known for her warm welcomes, not unless it was someone she wished to impress. Delivery boys didn't come into that category.

Ida couldn't quite hear what was being said, but madam was flapping her hand, then shaking a fist at the boy. Poor soul. He'd obviously done summat wrong. Happen he'd brought the wrong stuff from the shop.

'I'll deal with this, Ida,' she called back over her shoulder.

'Rightio, Madam.' Ida turned to go, but spotted a bunch of grapes sitting atop the fruit bowl on the hall sideboard, and was momentarily distracted while she popped one in her mouth, then another. What a treat! Fortunately the aunts were out, so no one would see her. She heard an angry shout and a cry but by the time she'd rearranged the grapes to cover the gap, the boy was gone and the front door had slammed shut. Ida scuttled back to the kitchen like a mouse into its hole.

By this time, Fanny had finished her story and Ida had missed the exciting part, as she so often did. Why was she always the one called upon to jump up and down to fetch things or answer the door, which on this occasion had been a complete waste of time?

''Oo was it, Ida?'

She bit into her scone and spoke through a shower of crumbs. 'Only a lad delivering summat for madam.'

'Nobody special then?'

'No.' Ida reached for another scone, anxious that they might all be gone before she'd finished this one, and got her hand slapped for her greed.

'Yer mouth is still full,' Mrs Petty chided her. 'Nay, I'll never manage to teach you manners, girl, not if I live to be a hundred.'

Ida flushed crimson, Mrs Petty being the nearest to a mother she'd ever known so she did her best to please. But it'd been mighty hard since Fanny left, and she missed Dennis teasing her, and even the smell of old Mr Askew's pipe. Nothing was quite as it used to be, in the good old days, as Mrs P was wont to call them.

Mrs Petty removed the plate from her reach. 'You can have another, Fanny love, and tell us how you're getting on with the mistress. Eeh, it's grand to see you. We get none of the gossip in these parts nowadays. What's she like as a boss, Kate O'Connor as was? Is she managing the factory well in the master's absence? We rarely see hide nor hair of her round here. Mind you, it's that poor child I feel sorry for. Left to her own devices more often than is good for her, poor little lamb. If it weren't for Madam Lucy, she'd be no better than an orphan.'

'Is that why the little lass looks so pasty-faced?' Fanny enquired, plastering jam on to a scone as if it might go out of fashion.

'Pasty-faced?' Mrs Petty looked affronted, taking offence at the implication the child wasn't properly fed. 'Nay, she eats everything I put in front of her.

You should see the breakfasts that child consumes. Two eggs at a time, no messing.'

Fanny shrugged. 'Pardon me for poking me nose in where it's not wanted, but I saw little Flora setting off to school after lunch and she looked a bit subdued like. A bit hang-dog you might say. No skipping about and running. Solemn little miss, I thought, holding on to her aunt's hand. Is she allus so quiet?'

Mrs Petty considered this question with a frown. 'Aye, happen she is a bit too serious. You hardly know she's there at times. Not normal really, for a child her age. I blame that mother of hers. That Kate O'Connor as was neglects her summat shocking, she does. Heartless floozy where her children are concerned, allus was. I've said as much often, have I not, Ida?'

'Yes, Mrs Petty.'

Fanny frowned, 'I thought you fancied her at one time fer the master? And he's got her, hasn't he? Tekken her as his wife, more's the wonder.'

Mrs Petty sniffed her disapproval, making her opinion on the matter abundantly clear. 'I did once think she might suit as his bit on the side, as you might say. The toffs go in for mistresses, don't you know. But never for a moment did I expect him to marry the brazen hussy. Well, I mean, it's not done, is it? 'Tain't right.'

'Aye, but he has done it. Done it proper, some might say.'

'It'll not last. Mark my words, it'll all end in tears. I've said so often, have I not, Ida?'

'Yes, Mrs Petty.' Ida had managed to sneak another scone on to her plate, so again sent a scattering of crumbs flying everywhere as she spoke, earning herself no more than a resigned shake of the head this time as Mrs Petty passed her a napkin.

Fanny surprised herself by defending her employer, stoutly pointing out how much of an effort it took to run a factory, particularly in war time. 'I don't see why he shouldn't marry her, if you want my opinion. This class business is a lot of old-fashioned stuff and nonsense. You'll see, it'll all be different once this war is over.'

'Well, I never! What's got into you?'

'And she can't be everywhere at once, now can she? Someone has to run that flippin' factory, so why not her? She's making a good job of it, s'matter of fact. I still say there's summat not quite right with that little miss though, and if I were you I'd keep a watchful eye on things. Look a bit closer to home, and see what's going on right under yer nose.'

'Eeh, do you think so, Fanny?' Mrs Petty asked, mouth hanging open in surprise.

'I do.'

—

The moment Lucy slammed the front door closed, she stormed upstairs to her bedroom and took out her temper on the pillows by ripping them to shreds, sending feathers flying everywhere. Drat and damn it, this was the last thing she'd expected. Dear God, how had he found them? She couldn't believe her bad luck.

She'd stared at the boy open-mouthed with horror for what seemed like a lifetime before she'd felt able to pull herself together sufficiently to think. And she'd certainly had to think fast. She'd heard Ida lurking in the passage behind her and swiftly realised that it wouldn't do for the boy to be spotted by any of the servants. Mrs Petty in particular would remember him well. So she'd called out to Ida, saying something about a delivery, that she'd deal with the matter. It was a miracle she'd bothered to answer the door in the first place, but the sound of that bell clanging on and on had quite frayed her nerves, and it had become patently obvious that no one else in the house was going to.

She'd known instantly who he was. For all it had been years since she'd set eyes on him, the likeness to his mother was uncanny.

Heaven help her, but it was fortunate that Kate had not been home. As always at this time of day, she was at the factory. Even more fortunate, little Flora was still at school and the aunts out paying calls.

Lucy began pacing the room, wringing her hands in agitation. What should she do? What should she do?

After Ida had gone, she'd very cleverly scolded the stupid boy for coming to the wrong house, just as if he really were a delivery boy. She'd boxed his ears and sent him packing. She therefore did not expect to see him again; not after the roasting she'd given him.

Lucy paused in her pacing to consider the situation more rationally and felt a film of perspiration break out on her brow, her hands grow clammy. What if he did come again though? What if he called when she wasn't in? What if Mrs Petty answered the door this time or, worse, Kate herself? Dear God, this was a disaster. All that time and effort, all these years of planning and patient waiting, and she could be right back where she'd started.

Lucy put her hands to her head, thoughts buzzing round and round like angry bees; none of them making any sense. Eliot had married the boy's mother. He'd rejected Lucy's own offer and made that little whore his *wife*, for God's sake! And he'd adopted Callum legally, so if the boy returned from the dead, as it were, they'd be able to play happy families all over again.

And her own children would get nothing!

All three of them would be out in cold with nothing to show for her efforts, despite all her planning and clever scheming. Lucy almost let out a scream of rage; was forced to bite down hard on her lip to prevent herself from doing so, since the noise would be sure to bring someone running to find out what on earth was wrong with her. She was going mad, that's what was wrong. Half demented with fury. There must be something she could do. But what? *What could she do?*

Lucy regretted sending the boy away now, since it left her with no idea what he might do next. She should have gone after him. Found out why he was here. Taken him someplace else, somewhere safer, somewhere from which there could be no return.

Should she go and look for him? No, that could be dangerous. He might not have recognised her, after all. Might stay away. Then again, he might not. *How could she be sure?* Oh, she was in a fever of indecision. Biting her nails, wringing her hands, scarring furious wheels along her arm with her own sharp nails, Lucy continued to rage helplessly about the room.

She'd *kill* the little bastard if she got half a chance. Wring the life out of his scrawny neck.

Lucy still hadn't thought of a solution some two hours later, despite turning the problem over and over in her head, considering every possibility, each new idea wilder than the last. Then it suddenly occurred to her that she was supposed to be collecting Flora from school, as she always did.

By the time she arrived, the child was nowhere in sight. Dear God, now she'd lost her, and would be in trouble for that too. Perhaps that was the answer, Lucy thought. She should get rid of Flora as well. But how? She couldn't take another child to the workhouse, not with the war on. They'd only ask if her daddy had been killed on the Somme and did her mother need special assistance to cope? Everything had changed now. The world had gone soft, become more caring. No, she would need to be taken somewhere far away, where no one would think to look. Somewhere much further than the Langdales.

'I'm here, I'm here, Aunt Lucy. I thought you'd forgotten me. I've been playing while I waited for you, but I've been a very good girl. Honest.'

Lucy grabbed Flora's hand and began to march her along the street. 'I don't believe you. You were very naughty to go wandering off like that. Didn't I tell you to stay and wait for me at the school gate? What your mother will say I cannot imagine.'

Flora began to cry. 'Don't tell Mammy I've been bad. Please don't. Mammy has to work for the war. You aren't going to smack me, Aunt Lucy, are you? I didn't wander off, honest I didn't. I was just…'

'Never mind what you were *just* doing. I've told you to stay by the school gate.' All the fury and frustration that had been building up inside her seemed to explode in that moment. How *dare* the child disobey? How *dare* that stupid boy have the effrontery simply to walk back into their lives? Lucy pushed Flora up a back street and swinging back her hand, slapped her with all her might. Flora screamed and fell over, knocking her head on a wall as she went down. She lay very still, not making a sound.

'Get up, child. Don't just lie there in the dirt. Get up, I say!' Flora didn't move, not even an eyelash fluttered. In that moment, Lucy realised that this time she'd gone too far.

–

'I really don't know where she is,' Lucy said, trying to appear concerned and anxious. 'I thought at first she was simply playing a game and hiding from me. I'll admit I was a little late getting to the school, but then I'd had so many interruptions this afternoon. Heaven knows what the servants do with their time, they are certainly never around when needed.'

Both the maiden aunts were looking troubled. Vera said, 'Do you think we should call out the police?'

'No, no, I'm quite certain she's playing some prank or other. Making me worry because I was late. I'm sure she'll turn up at any moment, chastened and apologetic, and so she should be. I, for one, shall certainly give that little miss a piece of my mind when she does.' And Lucy picked up her embroidery and proceeded to apply her needle. After a moment, Vera and Cissie did likewise, while the clock ticked on in the small parlour.

The sound of it pounded in Lucy's head like a drum.

But although all three women sat and waited for the better part of an hour, Flora did not arrive home from school, as Lucy had known that she would not. Cissie grew quite demented with worry, constantly getting up to look out of the parlour window, the dogs anxiously padding back and forth behind her on each occasion. Even Aunt Vera was fussing a great deal, constantly glancing up at the clock, or examining the silver fob watch she had pinned to the bodice of her woollen frock.

'Dear me, I'm beginning to think we should perhaps call the constabulary,' she began, when the door opened and Kate strolled in. She glanced about her, taking in their solemn expressions, and her usual sunny smile instantly faded. 'What is it? What's happened? Oh, God, it's Eliot.'

Cissie ran to her at once. 'No, no, my dear. Don't fret yourself. It's not dear Eliot at all. It's Flora. She's not yet home from school, that's all. She's being a naughty girl and is playing pranks on us. But it's true that we are all becoming just a little anxious about her.'

'Didn't you collect her as usual, Lucy?'

'Am I your maidservant? Good gracious me!'

'But that was our arrangement. We agreed. In fact, you offered.'

'Out of the goodness of my heart, since the child was obviously neglected. And, yes, I did indeed go to collect her, as I always do. She was not there. No sign of her waiting at the school gate, as there should have been. She's obviously run off to play some stupid game or other.'

Kate looked as if she might collapse and Cissie attempted to lead her to a chair, urging her to sit.

Kate shook her off. 'She would never do that. Oh, Lord, where can she be? Where the hell is she?'

'Don't you swear at me in that common way. I'll not have your workhouse manners in here.' Lucy had had ample time to think long and hard over the last hour and believed she had the answer to her problem. 'You are the one to blame here, not me. You are the one who neglects your own child and leaves her to the care of others. *And this isn't the first child you have lost, is it?*'

Aunt Vera let out a strangled gasp, reaching at once for her *sal volatile*.

'Oh, my word! Oh deary, deary me,' murmured Cissie, and then for the first time in her life put forward a question on her own behalf. 'Surely you aren't suggesting, Lucy, that this was all deliberate? That Kate would…' She quite ran out of words.

'That is exactly what I am saying. Who else had the opportunity? Who else would do such a terrible thing? Didn't this girl from Poor House Lane give away her own son for adoption, sell him in order to gain herself employment? And as if that weren't bad enough, she inveigled herself into Eliot's bed and got herself pregnant by him so that he felt duty bound to wed her. Now, having got her grasping little hands on his business and full control of his financial affairs, that child too has become a nuisance. She's disposed of her as swiftly and mercilessly as she did the other. First Callum, now Flora.'

'Oh, my goodness me,' said Aunt Vera, stunned by this turn of events.

'That is an abominable lie.' Kate could barely manage to get the words out, her throat felt so constricted, her fear so great. 'Tell me what has happened to Flora. Where is she?'

Lucy longed to say – 'lying dead in a gutter', but that would give the game away. Inside, she was glorying in her victory, unexpected perhaps but all the better for that. She felt jubilant, exhilarated. She'd thought she was about to lose everything but she'd won after all. She'd not only rid herself of both of those bastard children, but, if she had her way, would soon be rid of their dratted mother as well. There would be nothing then to stop her from having Eliot all to herself. He'd be as putty in her hands, only too willing for her to look after things for him. Lucy saw herself running the factory, with Jack, now fourteen, taking over in just a short year or two. Oh, it was all going to work out splendidly.

Kate said, 'Tell me! I'm waiting for you to tell me what has happened to Flora.'

Lucy straightened her spine, wrinkling her nose with distaste as she regarded her rival, just as if Kate were still that ragamuffin child who'd crawled out from one of Kendal's worst yards. 'Don't try to wriggle out of this. Your guilt is plain for all to see. What did you do with them both? Throw them in the river, as you probably did with that husband of yours, assuming you ever had one in the first place. Was that the way of it? Did you dispose of Callum's father too, once he was of no further use? Is that what you plan to do to Eliot?' She turned to Vera. 'Perhaps we should ask Ida to go for the police constable, after all, Aunt. This is all beginning to look dreadfully serious.'

For once in her life Vera seemed utterly incapable of making a decision of any sort. Cissie appeared as stunned as her sister, Kate frozen to the spot, white with shock. Lucy carelessly shrugged her shoulders and marched towards the door. 'Then I shall deal with the matter myself. See that she doesn't run away, Vera, while I find Ida.'

Long before she reached it, the door swung open, revealing none other than the child in question, face streaked with mud and blood in just about equal quantities, school gymslip torn, knees scraped but with a smile of pure delight on her young face.

'Mammy! Mammy!' cried Flora. 'Look who I've found. You remember that boy I told you about, my friend from the market with the fat lady? I found him sitting on a wall near my school. And what do you think, Mammy? He believes he already knows you. Does he Mammy? Do you know him?'

Chapter Ten

Did she know him? What a question? How could a mother not know her own child, even if she hadn't set eyes on him for more years than she cared to count? But then he wasn't a child any more. No longer the sturdy toddler she'd once cuddled on her lap, sung lullabies or read to from his *Little Stories for Little Folk*. Thirteen years old and on the verge of manhood, he was as tall as herself now, if more scrawny for his height than was healthy. Why was he so thin? Had he not been properly looked after? Where had he been? Why had he left? Why had he chosen to come home now, and not before? Or had he been held somewhere against his will? As these questions and a dozen others raced through her head, Kate stood rooted to the spot, frozen with shock, only vaguely aware of the other people in the room: of Vera making clucking noises of disbelief, Cissie quietly weeping, Flora hanging on to his arm as if she might never let go, and Lucy as pale and ghostlike as she must herself look.

'Mam, is it really you?' He was gazing at her with rapt attention, his bright eyes troubled yet filled with hope.

Kate tried to speak but no sound came out. She put a hand to her mouth, struggling for control, then tried again. 'Indeed it is, son.' She felt an urge to snatch him to her and yet, overawed by the strangeness of him, was quite unable to move a muscle.

He was frowning at her, the vaguest hint of hostility creeping over his handsome face. 'Why did you send me away? Why didn't you want me no more?'

It was as if a hand had taken her heart and squeezed the life out of it, leaving her momentarily breathless. 'Sure, and of course I wanted you. I never sent you away, m'cushla. Haven't I spent the last eight years searching for ye, hunting high and low in the desperate hope I'd find you again? Why in God's name did you run off in the first place?'

'I didn't run off. I was *taken*!'

A muted gasp from the aunts while Kate felt her knees give way, forcing her to sink on to a nearby chair.

'I was told you didn't love me no more, that you wanted rid of me.'

Kate gave a low moan, eyes filling with unshed tears as she slowly shook her head, lips trembling as she whispered, '*Never!*'

There followed a long drawn-out silence, one filled with the pain of those lost years, in which the emotion in that small parlour was palpable, almost too much to bear.

In a voice raw with agony, quite unlike her own, Kate asked, 'Who told you that? Taken by whom? God in heaven, Callum love, will ye tell us where've you been all this time?'

And then seemingly in slow motion, Callum's eyes swivelled round to Lucy. 'Ask her. She knows everything.'

Not understanding, Kate frowned. 'How can Lucy know? Have ye told yer aunt already, before ye'd tell yer own mam? Aw, Callum sweetheart, don't break me heart again.'

He was vigorously shaking his head. 'I don't need to tell her. She knows already. Mebbe she planned it all from the start.' As he said this, he instinctively put a protective arm about his half-sister's shoulders and Flora hugged him tight. '*She* took me away. I couldn't remember anything till I come to t'market again today and walked over that bridge. Me feet found this house and the minute *that woman* opened the door, it all came flooding back. Like a bad dream, the nightmare what runs in me head over and over. And from the state of Flora here, you can see she wasn't satisfied with ruining my life, she intended to ruin the bairn's as well.'

Mind in a whirl, only then did Kate think to look upon her daughter and her heart clenched with fresh fear. Hair matted with blood, bruises on her lovely face, Flora looked as if she'd been beaten black and blue. Kate blinked in disbelief. 'What on earth...?'

Thrusting herself forward, Lucy tossed her head in that arrogant way she had. '*He* attacked her, of course.'

'*I* attacked her? Nay, that's rich, that is. I were the one what found her up that alley where you left her. I *saved* her. What were you going to do to the wee bairn after you'd thumped her, take *her* to t'workhouse an' all, or were you hoping she were a goner?'

Kate looked at Lucy with eyes dazed in bewilderment. 'What is he trying to say? What's all this about an alley, and the workhouse? Do you understand a word of it?'

'Course she understands.' Callum pointed an accusing finger. '*She* were the one! It was *her* what took me away that day, give me a good hiding and dumped me in t'Union Workhouse. I thought I'd struck lucky when I were sent up to that farm in the Langdales, but the Brocklebanks weren't kindly folk. Fer all I know, *she* might've had a hand in that an' all.'

'He's lying!' Lucy snapped, spitting the words in the boy's face, fingers curling with fury as if she itched to scratch his eyes out. 'What else would you expect from a workhouse brat?'

'Calm yourself, Lucy,' instructed Aunt Vera in her sternest tones.

'Oh, deary, deary me,' echoed Cissie, wringing her hands.

Callum was growing agitated, his now quite deep voice rising on a note of desperation as he stood before a bemused Kate. 'Ask Flora then, if you don't believe me. Ask your daughter.'

It was all too much for Kate to take in. Had she lost him? Was it far too late for them ever to be close again? When she'd dreamed of this moment it hadn't been anything like this. Why weren't they hugging each other? Why wasn't he weeping in her arms, glad to be home? Kate knew it wasn't unusual for a child to blame its mother if it got lost. Was this his way of dealing with it all, by placing the blame on someone else, first on herself, and now on Lucy? She put out a hand, wanting to soothe him, to calm this beloved son of hers with the assurance that she did indeed love him, but he brushed her hand aside. Beside him, Flora was ashen, which made the cuts and bruises on her small, pinched face stand out more livid than ever.

'Is this true, Flora? Did someone hurt you? Was it…?' Kate couldn't find the words. She'd trusted Lucy. Despite her initial doubts, largely due to her sister-in-law's innate snobbishness, yet she'd come round to accepting the woman's help, pushing aside the guilt all working mothers feel when leaving the care of their child to another. But Kate had to know the truth. She had to understand what, if anything, Lucy had done. Could this stuck-up sister-in-law who'd viewed her with contempt from the start, constantly scorning and disparaging her because of her humble origins, truly have set out to steal and damage both her children?

Flora glanced fearfully up at her aunt then burst into tears. Nothing could have been more damning.

Kate got slowly to her feet, an eerie calmness creeping over her. It must be true then. *This woman had indeed hurt her children!* But why would she do such a thing? And then the answer came. She'd done it out of jealousy, from fear of losing what she considered to be her own children's inheritance. And she still blamed Eliot for Charles's suicide.

The gaze Kate turned upon Lucy now was ice cold. 'Mother of God, what an unholy mess.'

'Don't you dare look at me in that condemning way, you Irish whore! Who are *you* to judge *me*? Your children deserved everything that happened to them, no worse than they received at your own hand, feckless, selfish mother that you are.'

Kate had never felt more calm, more in control, instinct warning her that this was not the moment for unleashing her fiery Irish temper, although she might well inwardly burn to defend herself. 'It's true then. You abducted Callum, and today battered Flora. Do you deny it?'

'Why should I? A doxy like you deserves everything you get.'

There was a collected intake of breath at this confession.

Callum leapt forward, scarlet in the face with outrage. 'Don't you call my mother names or you'll have me to reckon with. You're the villain here, the nastiest piece of work I ever clapped eyes on, and I've seen some bad 'uns in me time. Nobody could call the workhouse easy, and the Brocklebanks weren't soft either but then they weren't gentlefolk, not like you. You're supposed to know better.'

Kate rested a calming hand on her son's shoulder. This time he didn't shrug it off, but let it lie. Entirely ignoring Lucy, she quietly addressed the aunts. 'Whatever the truth of this matter, Flora's wounds need attention. Cissie, perhaps you would...'

'Of course, of course. Come along, Flora dear. Come to your Aunty Cissie.' And Flora willingly flung herself into the comfort of the doggy-scented embrace, sobbing her heart out.

'Go with her,' Kate urged Callum, but he stubbornly shook his head.

'I'm staying here, with you.' Their eyes met and a flicker of hope stirred in Kate's heart. Perhaps it wasn't too late after all, and she hadn't quite lost him.

'I trust we can keep this matter in the family?' Vera quietly warned, meaning she had no wish for any further gossip to be inflicted upon them. Neither had Kate.

Callum gasped. 'Nay, aren't we going to call the coppers in? She should be prosecuted, locked up.'

Deep down Kate agreed with him, yet knew Vera made a valid point. Hadn't they all had a bellyful of rumour and scandal already? Were she to even try to get Lucy arrested, as Callum suggested, it could easily backfire upon herself, knowing how clever and manipulating she could be. Even now Lucy had that satisfied smirk upon her face, knowing she was untouchable. And Kate still saw herself as the girl from Poor House Lane, for all she was now a respectable married woman. 'I shan't make any decisions on that score until Eliot comes home,' she told the older woman, and Vera nodded her approval.

With the aunts and Flora gone, Kate drew in a steadying breath, clenching her fists in an effort to hold on to her hard-won restraint as she faced her sister-in-law. 'So did it give you satisfaction to watch me pine for me lovely boy, knowing all the time where he was?'

Lucy laughed. 'It was at times most entertaining.'

A pain clenched Kate's heart as she thought of the anguish this woman had put her through. 'What kind of woman are you? What sort of mother?'

'One who would go to any lengths, *any lengths*, not to see her own children disinherited,' Lucy hissed.

'I have no idea whether or not they should inherit. That is a decision only Eliot can make, which he will do in the fullness of time when this war is won. For now, I'd be obliged if you would pack your bags and leave his house. I don't want you any longer under his roof, under *our* roof.'

Kate felt some small degree of satisfaction as she saw the colour drain from her sister-in-law's cheeks, the tightness of Lucy's jawline slacken in disbelief.

And was that fear lurking in her troubled gaze? 'You surely aren't casting me out into the streets?'

'Think yourself fortunate you won't be spending the night under lock and key in a jail cell. I just hope that I don't come to regret my generosity.'

'You aren't being in the least generous,' Lucy snapped. 'Where do you expect me to sleep? I don't have any other home to go to. And how will I eat?'

'Well now, the Kirkland Poor House is closed, as ye know, so mebbe you could try the Union Workhouse on Kendal Green, since you're so well acquainted with the guardians there.' She heard Callum's soft chuckle and gently squeezed his shoulder, warning him to hush, before crossing the room and throwing open the parlour door. 'For all I care, you can sleep in the gutter. You're no longer welcome in this house. Your allowance will continue to be paid, for the time being at least, on condition that you stay away; that you never come near my children ever again. When Eliot returns, once he's been given the full facts, he will no doubt make a decision on whether or not you should be punished, or deserve to receive any further assistance from the company. You did, after all, attempt to destroy his family.'

The violet eyes flashed, revealing panic for the first time, yet Lucy remained obstinately defiant. 'You think he'd abandon *me*, that he'd take *your* word against mine, a whore against a Tyson? Never!'

Kate smiled. 'You're only a Tyson by marriage, as am I. But yes, I think he might well take my word, and that of his son, don't you? He'll be only too delighted to have Callum home safe and well, and you know it.'

'You'd poison his mind against me?'

'Oh, I think you've achieved that all on your own, without any assistance from me. And don't see this as weakness on my part, or as any sign of forgiveness. No one abuses my children and gets away with it. But neither will I allow evil to flourish under my roof. So pack yer bags and leave. Now!'

–

Mrs Petty declared, and Ida and Fanny heartily agreed, that they hadn't enjoyed a more entertaining afternoon in years at Tyson Lodge. The raised voices in the parlour had naturally attracted their attention, bringing them creeping out into the hall so they could all the better hear what was going on. There'd been a slight interruption when the aunts had appeared with a sorry-looking Flora, and Ida was duly dispatched to fetch hot water and iodine. Cissie carried the child upstairs while Mrs Petty, Fanny and Miss Vera remained in the hall, ears pricked.

Sadly, the exchange in the parlour had become somewhat muted so that they were forced to draw ever nearer in an effort to hear properly. Fanny swore that if blood looked like being drawn, she'd swallow her pride and run for Dennis. Ida, having scooted to the kitchen, drawn the hot water, flown up the stairs and back in record time, quickly returned to join the curious eavesdroppers.

Mrs Petty felt quite certain that at any moment Miss Vera would notice their presence, scold them all and send them scurrying back into the kitchen. But she did nothing of the sort, being far too busy cocking an ear herself. And then the door was flung wide and they all had to quickly dip back into the shadows.

The voices within rang out loud and clear, all about the wickedness done to those poor children by madam Lucy, of her being cast out into the streets and there being no chance of forgiveness, which Mrs Petty later declared was too good for her by half and she should be hung, drawn and quartered at the very least.

Then Lucy stormed into the hall, a veritable dervish of fury, ordering Ida to pack her bags, and Fanny to fetch a cab as she refused to stay a moment longer in this house simply to be insulted. Not a soul among them moved an inch.

'*Do you hear what I say*?' Lucy screamed, stamping her foot and going red, white and all shades of purple by turn.

It was Vera who had the temerity to step forward. 'I believe no one is preventing you from leaving, Lucy. And perhaps, in the circumstances, it would be for the best. As ye sow, so shall ye reap.'

Lucy had no option but to obey. She stormed upstairs to her room where she was obliged to pack her own bags and stagger down the stairs with them moments later before the humiliating gaze of the entire household. No punishment by the judicial system could have been more devastating at that moment, no departure more demeaning for a woman so obsessed with her own status. For her fall from grace to be witnessed by everyone, including the servants, in condemning silence, was utterly mortifying.

Not a soul offered to open the door for her, and Lucy found herself out in the porch with not even a cab waiting, her instructions on this completely ignored. She was forced to abandon most of her luggage and walk to the station, although where she would go after that, she really hadn't the first idea.

And as the door swung closed on her furious, departing figure, Kate turned to Callum and held wide her arms. 'Welcome home, son.' And grinning from ear to ear, he walked into them to hug his mother tight.

Chapter Eleven

1919

The woman ran through the gathering crowds on to the station platform, the wind ruffling her red hair, slapping it across her face as she struggled to pin her hat in place. People stepped out of her way with a smile, seeing how flustered she was. She was not the first to appear thus on this particular morning, except that this woman seemed different from most, her slender body erect with pride, her bearing one of dignity and grace despite her anxiety.

She was regarding the train that stood puffing quietly at the platform with a mixture of outrage and defiance, as if it had no right to be there, and yet there was pain too, an agony in those soft grey eyes which made people turn away and pretend to concern themselves with the cloudy skies or a brown paper bag being blown along by the chill spring breeze.

The woman grabbed a porter. 'Is this the London train?'

'It was last time I looked.'

'When did it arrive?'

'Five minutes ago, six mebbe. The twelve-ten, running on time.'

Five minutes. Time enough for him to realise that she wasn't there waiting for him, as she had promised. Time for him to wander off looking for her, perhaps? Kate glanced about, growing ever more frantic as the crowd thinned and people began to move away. Where could he be? What if he hadn't even been on the train at all? Oh, my darling, let nothing happen now to prevent our glorious reunion.

The men looking on couldn't help wishing it were them she had rushed to see with such anxiety in her lovely face, while the women envied her sense of style, and that natural beauty which meant she could still look stunning, even with no hat and her hair blowing everywhere.

She finally got the offending article in place, although the women tut-tutted when they saw that she did not possess a hat pin with which to anchor it. Consequently, mere seconds later it was knocked awry as a young soldier rushed past to gather his sweetheart tight in his arms, and they heard her cry out with despair.

Would her soldier come?

Kate Tyson stopped running and smoothed down her coat. Giving up on the hat, she tidied the rebellious red curls as best she could, pinning the mass of them back with a comb and a few hair grips, tucking a stray strand behind each ear.

Her two-piece was of blue linen with semi-raglan sleeves and a high buttoned collar. The shoes, of course, were of the finest kid leather with the latest and fashionably high Louis heels. Most of all he would notice the shoes, and hopefully her trim ankles. Kate had spent hours getting ready, so wanting to look her best.

If only Flora hadn't kicked up such a fuss at break-fast time or Aunt Vera hadn't launched into one of her interminable lectures, she would have been on time. Now here she was, despite all her best efforts, arriving late on a draughty station platform, heart beating like a drum, sick with nerves and shaking in every limb.

Where was he? Where was he?

He would think she'd forgotten, that she hadn't come.

There wasn't even a band playing in welcome. So different from the day on which she'd first seen Eliot off to war, four long years ago. On that day there'd been a mood of celebration, certainly high optimism. The town band had played, the Mayor and his good lady handing out gifts and parcels of food to the new recruits taking the King's shilling. Almost as if the war were nothing more than a game which would soon be won and they'd all be back home with their loved ones by Christmas.

But Christmas had come and gone and the war had dragged on. Too many of those bright, hand-some young men never would return.

On the day he'd joined up, Kate and Eliot had been very much at odds, not having spoken to each other for some years. Yet her love for him, even then, had overridden all their differences and she'd been unable to resist coming to see him off.

That had been the day when she had admitted that Flora, her darling daughter, was indeed Eliot's child, and later he'd come home on leave to make Kate his wife. Oh, she'd kicked up quite a fuss over that, had denied she needed him, but she couldn't ever deny her love for him and so they had married, a joyous day with all their friends present and Flora as bridesmaid.

Now Flora was a precocious ten-year-old and had thrown one of her tantrums at not being allowed to accompany her mother to the station, but Kate had been adamant. Her first meeting with Eliot after so long a separation must be private. They needed to be alone.

Bad enough that they must return to a house full of gossiping servants, not to mention his two aunts who, dear as they were, could be extremely intrusive.

And there was so much to tell him, so many details she had kept from him while he was serving King and country. Facts about the business, for a start, that would now need to be revealed with great tact and care. And quite how that would be achieved, Kate had no real idea, frowning with new anxiety at the thought.

But there was much more to be explained than problems with the business. Eliot knew that Callum, his adopted son, was safely home again, but Kate had never properly explained how that had come about, deciding it was something best told in person rather than a letter. She would simply have to play it by ear, make her judgements according to his reaction to the changes that had taken place in his absence.

Kate felt a small nub of worry in the pit of her stomach when she thought of the reunion between man and boy. Eliot had always loved him as his own, but how would Callum react?

The crowds were moving away, families holding their loved one close, children carried high in their fathers' arms, some of them crying, not recognising this stranger who had burst into their lives.

Heart beating a little faster, Kate clenched her gloved hands tight. What would she say to her husband? Would they feel like strangers or reunited lovers? How would it feel to have him hold her again?

She momentarily closed her eyes on a rush of memory, remembering the glorious pressure of his body against hers, the warm touch of his hand, the roughness of his chin when he took her in a compelling kiss. Would she be shy like a young bride, or eager and passionate? To her shame, Kate rather thought it would be the latter.

'Step back miss, if you please.'

All such concerns were wiped from her mind as the station porter waved his green flag, doors slammed, a whistle blew and the next instant the train let out a great sigh and belch of steam, then slowly began to move out of the station. It was leaving, and still she hadn't found him. Kate was running alongside it, checking every window. Could Eliot still be on board, fallen asleep perhaps, or leaving again because she hadn't been here to meet him? No, no, he would never do that, surely. And then the train was gone, the platform was quite empty and she was alone.

—

Kate sat in the parlour at Tyson Lodge and rocked herself in misery as the tears flowed unchecked down her cheeks. Lunch was over, the appetites of the two aunts, at least, not spoiled by anxiety as they had devoured several slices of bread and butter, boiled ham and tomatoes, and still Eliot had not come. Kate had been quite unable to eat a thing. But then, this was not at all how she had planned things.

'Where is he? Why didn't he wait? Admittedly the train arrived five or six minutes before I did, but where could he have disappeared to in that short time? He can't have been on the train. Do you think he hasn't come at all? Oh, I can't bear the thought of something going wrong now, at this late stage.'

Aunt Vera frowned at Kate over her spectacles. 'Stop fretting, child. What could possibly go wrong?

He probably missed that train and will be on the next. He is safe and well, be thankful for that. Our darling Eliot has survived the war and will soon be home in the bosom of his family where he belongs.'

'Do you think so?' Fresh hope began to glow inside Kate, masking her irritation that as a young matron of thirty-two she should still be addressed as if she were a child. Typical of Vera's stern view of life, except that she was right in a way. Kate had been fretting for days.

But then, she'd wanted everything to be perfect for Eliot's homecoming.

Kate had been up since dawn making things ready, helping Mrs Petty prepare food for a celebration like no other. In the last week Tyson Lodge had been turned inside out, every room scrubbed and polished and dusted, carpets beaten, vases filled with fresh flowers, everything in Eliot's study arranged just as he liked it with his favourite pen in its holder, a brand new blotter on the leather topped desk, and the latest balance sheets from the factory waiting for him to peruse at his leisure.

Kate herself had occupied this room for much of the war and a part of her wondered how it would feel to relinquish it after all this time, to give up her managerial role at Tyson's Shoes and return all decision-making to the factory's owner. Even the small business of making army boots she herself had started, successful though it undoubtedly was, had been swallowed up by Tyson's during the war years, the two merged into one since that had been the best way to deal with things.

She still had a few little plans for the business buzzing at the back of her mind. Well, not so little, as a matter of fact. One in particular that she'd been toying with for some time.

Oh, but if Eliot didn't approve, she'd give it up, and gladly. She really wouldn't object to being totally free from all responsibility. Kate could then devote her time simply to being a wife and making Eliot happy. She ached to hold him in her arms again, to love him.

Besides, she would not be alone in this change of circumstance. Since the Great War had ended, those women fortunate enough to have their menfolk returned to them – women who had worked not only in Tyson's Kendal shoe factory but had kept the local transport running, farmed the land, produced the weapons and equipment to keep their men at the front, all working at tasks women had never before tackled – must now learn to take a back seat, to be content once more with being wives and mothers.

Dragging her mind back from the years of war work, she focused instead upon the present and the question Aunt Vera was asking.

'Does she know? Is Lucy aware that Eliot arrives home today?'

'I wouldn't know.'

'Someone, one of her friends perhaps, might have mentioned it.'

'Oh, indeed,' agreed Aunt Cissie, ever her sister's echo. 'You must be prepared for her to call, Kate.'

Vera continued, 'Sooner or later she will want to see him. He is her brother-in-law after all. If nothing else, she will wish to ensure that her allowance will continue, and may then give her version of – of events. Have you considered that?'

'I've no wish to consider Lucy at all, and certainly not today, Aunt.'

'Of course not, but I felt I should mention it – warn you. She is so jealous of you that she will want to put her case. How will you cope when she does call?'

Cissie's eyes grew round with sympathy. 'Oh, my dear, yes. How will you cope?'

'I shall not receive her. Why should I?'

'Have you told Eliot yet about what she did – or rather what we believe she did? What she is alleged to have done?'

Still that faint doubt, despite everything they'd palpably suffered at Lucy's hands.

Before Kate had time to frame an answer, if indeed there was one to give, the house echoed with the rattle and clang of the front door bell.

Kate was on her feet in a second. 'There he is! He's here at last, I know it.'

She was running through the hall, anxious to reach the door before Ida or Mrs Petty got there before her. The bell was impatiently ringing a second time even as she flung the door open and, like a miracle, there he stood, his lovely, handsome face wreathed in smiles. Kate stepped forward, ready to fling herself into her husband's arms, and then she saw that he was not alone.

'Look who I found waiting for me at the station,' Eliot said. 'Lucy. Just as well since I must have missed you. Couldn't spot you anywhere.'

Chapter Twelve

She had let him down. The reunion Kate had dreamed of for so long had all gone terribly wrong. Far more wrong than even Eliot appreciated. It was true that the minute they were alone, in their bedroom, he eagerly took her in his arms and kissed her with all the passion, all the love, she could wish for. Desire flared in her, as hot and strong as ever, but the hurt was there too, like a burr beneath the skin.

'Where did you go? Why didn't you wait?' she demanded, between kisses.

'More to the point, where were you, my darling? Did you forget I was arriving home today?'

He pulled her close and when she could catch her breath again, Kate pushed him gently away to frown at him with mock severity. 'How could I forget when I've been longing for this day for weeks… months? What a thing to say! Haven't we been up since dawn getting ready? Mrs Petty has been cooking and baking for days. I do hope you're hungry?'

'Not terribly. Lucy insisted on buying me lunch.'

Kate's heart sank even further, if that were possible, then rallied quickly on a spurt of anger. 'And you let her, knowing we were all waiting for you at home?'

Eliot laughed, and the dark eyebrows lifted in that mildly scolding way of his, the kind of look which firmly reminded her that he was the master here and could do as he pleased. For an instant Kate forgot that she was his beloved wife and felt as if she were still that struggling girl from Poor House Lane.

'I didn't know any such thing. The train came in and you, my dear wife, were not on the platform. Lucy explained how you'd been held up and...'

'She *what*?'

'Don't look so guilty, Kate. I forgive you.'

''Tis not guilt I feel, 'tis fury at her lies! Didn't I miss you by no more than a few minutes? The porter told me the train had only just arrived.'

Her soft Irish brogue had surfaced as it always did when Kate was annoyed and he smiled, enjoying this show of temper. She slipped from his embrace and her stance now was one of pride and obstinate defiance, which he knew only too well. 'Let me look at you, Kate. Dear heaven, I swear you are lovelier than ever, despite the storm brewing in those lovely grey eyes of yours.'

'And haven't I every right to be cross, with you wandering off for no reason at all?'

He chuckled, drawing her to him so he could savour the scent of her: lemon verbena shampoo, the tang of soap, and that special something which was uniquely Kate. 'I remember you looking every bit as truculent and defiant the very first day I saw you, when you were ready to take me to task for allowing my foreman to sack your rapscallion of a brother. I swear I was overawed by your beauty even then: by the set of that small square chin, the way your nostrils flared with temper, those lovely eyebrows winging defiantly upwards. Ready to take on the world and do battle. I swear you made me tremble.'

'I did no such thing.' She could feel herself softening beneath his charm, the tug of a smile at the corners of her mouth.

'No need to make excuses, my darling. I know how hard you have worked, how overwhelming it must have been for you, taking care of everything. You are safely relieved of all that worry now. I am home again, so what does it matter if you were too busy to come and collect me?'

'Sure and it matters to me. I'll not have Lucy say what isn't true. I didn't forget and I wasn't at all *too busy*! She's just looking for any excuse to stir up trouble between us.'

'Nonsense! Why would she do such a thing? Lucy was only being kind.'

'She was not being kind, she...' But the look in Eliot's eye silenced her, made her bite her lip and not embark upon her tale, not just now, not like this. Hadn't he only this very minute arrived home, and here they were quarrelling already? And if Lucy's actions had caused their quarrel, then hadn't she succeeded in her malice? Kate gave a small choking sob and fell into his arms. 'This isn't how I planned it. I so desperately wanted our reunion to be perfect, to be joyous.'

He stroked a damp tendril of hair from her hot cheek. 'And it is, my love. It is. I'm here, aren't I? We're together at last.'

She lifted her face for his kiss. Oh, why hadn't she told him the whole story from the start? It had seemed impossible at the time, cruel almost, to bother him with domestic issues while he was away fighting a war, when he might be killed at any moment and not in a position to do anything about the problems at home.

Now that dreadful woman threatened to rob Kate of happiness yet again.

Eliot looked so desperately tired. His sensitive mouth seemed to have thinned, with deep grooves marking each corner. The hawk-like nose was even more pronounced and the once fine bone structure more drawn, skin yellowed and pale. Was it any wonder after what he'd been through? He was thinner, looked much older than the day he'd gone off to war. Kate had noticed that he moved with a stiffness to his gait, favouring one leg. She'd made no comment upon this, hoping he would tell her of the injury that had caused it when he was good and ready. His hands might be calloused and scarred but they touched her cheek with the same tenderness as before, the velvet brown eyes resting on her with love. Kate was content.

'There is so much we need to talk about, so much I have to tell you.'

'And I you. That I love you still, that we have all the time in the world now, my darling, to be together. Don't be cross with me for not waiting. Or with Lucy for booking us lunch at the County. I believed that you'd encountered some problem at the works. And it was a very hasty luncheon, I didn't even pause to partake of a dessert, or coffee, though Lucy urged me to have one or the other. Then she drove me swiftly home in her fine motor, her latest acquisition no doubt. Apparently business is booming, which is good to hear. But never mind all of that now. I will gladly forgive you everything, if only you'll let me kiss you again, and again, and again.'

He began to suit actions to his words and how could she remain cross when he was kissing her face, her eyes, her throat, unbuttoning the high neck of her jacket, seeking the tender warmth of her breasts?

'Let me warm myself on your radiance. Kate, I have missed you so desperately.'

Kate bit back the bitter disappointment, dampened her anger over Lucy's lies and machinations, and allowed herself to be swept away by a different sort of storm altogether.

Later, as they lay naked together in the big wide bed, sated and happy, Eliot softly stroking her hair, she told him everything. The day Callum had apparently vanished off the face of the earth; one moment playing on the lawns, the next gone from their lives, would live forever in both their hearts. And they each suffered from the guilty knowledge that at the precise moment of his disappearance, they were paying him no attention at all but rather engaged in one of their spats.

If passion characterised their love affair, it had also blighted it in many ways. They had disagreed on all manner of topics, not least politics and the manner in which Eliot ran the business.

But then Kate had never been the kind of woman to surrender her independence, or subjugate her own opinion to any man's. On the day that Callum disappeared she'd been standing her corner for the sake of a friend, Millie, who was being badly abused by Ned Swainson, Eliot's crooked foreman. Kate's antipathy to the man had a long history, dating from the time he'd tried it on with her, and sacked her brother. Knowing this, Eliot had been inclined to believe that she was exaggerating in her account of his foreman's vicious behaviour. This had enraged Kate, and during the heated argument that followed, her son had apparently wandered out of the garden and disappeared.

Following the terrible discovery that Callum had vanished, without anyone seeing him go, Kate had almost lost her reason. She'd searched for her son for years, her heart breaking from her need to find him.

Now she was able to reveal exactly what had taken place; the whole sorry story. Kate gently and calmly explained to Eliot that Lucy, his sister-in-law, was the one responsible. She'd taken revenge over the suicide of her wastrel husband, Charlie, blaming Eliot entirely for his brother's untimely death because he'd adopted Kate's son, a child from Poor House Lane, thereby disinheriting his own family, in her opinion. And she'd done it in the most cruel way: by abducting the boy.

'She muddied his smart new clothes and slapped him, labelled him with a new name, Allan, sounding enough like his own to confuse a distressed five-year-old child. Then she took him to the Union workhouse on Kendal Green, and from there he was moved to Brocklebank's farm out on the Langdales. The couple were not kindly disposed towards him, since he was but an orphan farm boy in their eyes. Callum suffered badly at their hands.'

Eliot listened to all of this with increasing horror. 'I find this hard to believe. Absolutely incredible!'

'Nevertheless it is true.'

'How can you be certain? Has she confessed?'

'Of course she didn't confess. I learned of it from Callum himself. All those years I spent searching for him, and on one occasion, unbeknown to me, I came so close to finding him. He was apparently helping Mrs Brocklebank on Kendal market and while I was busy buying from another stall, Flora began to chat with him, offered him some of her barley sugar. I scolded her for talking to strangers. But I didn't know! I didn't know it was Callum. I saw a woman berating a young boy as we moved away, but I didn't get a clear view of him. Oh, if only I had.'

'Kate, my darling, how dreadful for you.'

'It tears me apart to think of it even now, to have been so close and not to have realised. Imagine what he had to endure: made to live in the barn with the animals, fed on scraps from their table, forced to work all hours and be shown not an ounce of love or pity. How can I live with that knowledge? It fills me with pain, with unendurable guilt.'

Eliot put his arms about her and held her tight as she quietly wept. 'We will not think any more of this matter right now. We will simply be glad that our boy is returned to us. I cannot wait to meet him, so don't you think, my darling, that it is time we rose and faced the world?'

She lifted her face to his one more time, still wet with tears, and he was so moved by the sight of her that he must love her all over again.

He ran a bath, peeled off his clothes and climbed into it with her. There were angry purple scars on his right leg and he lowered himself into the water with care, but since he made no remark upon them, neither did she. He soaped her back, her breasts, teasing and tickling her. Kate wriggled forward to sit astride his lap, arching her back in sheer ecstasy as she rode him, but then remembered the injured leg.

'Oh, I must take care, I don't want to hurt you.'

'Don't worry, you aren't, and I need you so badly, Kate.'

'Is that all right?'

'It is bliss.'

Yet insufficient for his urgent needs so he lifted her bodily from the rapidly cooling water, lay her down on the bathroom rug and took her with the kind of force that left them both gasping.

–

It was late afternoon when they finally emerged into the sitting room where the family were assembled, Kate quite flushed about the cheeks, Eliot looking remarkably pleased with himself.

The aunts were seated side by side on the sofa, for once not in their customary black but dressed in their best navy-blue chenille, to celebrate the occasion. Flora looked remarkably demure in a new white organza dress, though was sitting on the edge of her seat as if it were a huge effort for her to remain still.

With some relief, Kate noted that Lucy had shown the good sense not to enter the house, for all she'd clearly been anxious to see Eliot on his first day home. But then she hadn't been allowed to set foot in Tyson Lodge since the day Kate had turned her out of the family home and had publicly humiliated her before the servants.

However, as Aunt Vera had warned, she might well attempt to return now, hell-bent on trouble, making Kate regret the mercy she'd shown on that fateful day by not reporting her sister-in-law to the police for abducting a child.

Not that she would allow Lucy to spoil this red-letter day for one moment longer. This was the day Kate had dreamed of for so long. Even as Eliot kissed each aunt on the cheek and hugged and kissed his daughter, remarking on how much she'd grown and how pretty she was, making Flora giggle with plea-sure, his gaze was riveted upon Callum, his adopted son and Kate's own first-born.

Kate's heart swelled with pride just to look at Callum.

Wasn't he a fine young man? He was tall for his sixteen years, well made and strong and, in her eyes at least, remarkably handsome. The unruly thatch of hair was less fiery than her own, but its redness undoubtedly marked him as her son. His eyes were an enchanting blue-grey, slightly narrowed in that brooding way he had, and the mouth still tremulous and sulky as a child's. He reminded her very much of her own brother Dermot, which she hoped and prayed didn't bode ill.

He was leaning against one corner of the mantel-piece, seeming to indicate that he was on the fringes of this little group, this family, and really wished to play no part in it. She itched to tell him to take his hands out of his pocket and greet his father with better manners, but she held her tongue. This wasn't the moment for maternal nagging.

Eliot strode right over to him and grasped him by the shoulders, giving him a hearty hug and several paternal slaps on the back. 'Callum, I can't tell you how it warms my heart to see you, son! What good fortune that we are both returned home again, safe and well.'

There was a short silence during which Callum did indeed pull his hands from his pockets and stand erect, but only to move away from Eliot. When he spoke, his voice was soft, a chilling whisper. 'I am not your son, and never will be.'

Chapter Thirteen

Only Kate was privy to the flash of hurt that crossed her husband's face. 'Callum, don't say such a thing!' she chided him. 'Of course you are his son. Didn't Eliot and Amelia, your late mama, adopt you as a baby?'

Callum kept his gaze steady on Eliot for a full half minute before redirecting it to Kate. 'You always told me, Mother, that *my* father drowned in the River Kent during a flood.'

'Well, to be sure that is so, but…'

'And having lived most of me life on a remote farm in the Langdales as little more than an unpaid slave, why would I see this man as me dad? I don't know him. He's nobbut a stranger to me. Some bit of paper dun't turn a person into a father.'

Kate was horrified. She heard the aunts give a collective gasp and even Flora's excited chatter was stilled. This reunion seemed destined to go wrong. 'Callum, that's a terrible thing to say. Take it back, this minute.'

'No, no, the boy has a point,' Eliot quietly conceded. 'He's right. Being accepted as a parent is more than just a legal process. Sadly, due to circumstances beyond our control, we have indeed turned into strangers. But it was not always so and I hope to rectify the situation, with effect from now. I am certainly eager to do my part. I hope you feel the same, son?'

'Me name's Callum.'

Another short silence during which Kate could tell Eliot was struggling to quell a burst of irritation. 'Very well, as I say, I've taken your point. I trust we can at least be friends?' He held out his hand and only when it became obvious that Callum was not about to take it, did he let it fall again to his side. Eliot quickly adopted a brisk manner. 'Right, time to sample this feast which Mrs Petty and her stalwart band have taken such trouble to prepare. Shall we go through to the dining room?'

Flora bounced to his side. 'May I go in with you, Papa?'

'Most certainly, my sweet. I shall take great pleasure in escorting so charming a daughter.' And he proffered his arm for the giggling child to take.

Smiling with relief, Kate turned to Callum, expecting him to do the same for her, but he simply strode past her, his stubborn chin held high, and she was forced to enter the dining room alone.

From the day she'd found him standing on the doorstep two years ago, his attitude had been steadfastly obstructive. Kate was disappointed, and although she tried to make allowances it was immensely frustrating at times.

At fourteen he'd been at that awkward stage of adolescent self-consciousness where he could see nobody's point of view but his own. He'd felt betrayed, neglected, abandoned by his own mother, seeing himself as someone nobody cared for. And Kate could hardly blame him for feeling that way.

She'd agreed to let him be adopted by Eliot Tyson and his wife when he'd been barely fifteen months old because she'd feared her child might otherwise die of one of the myriad diseases easily contracted in Poor House Lane, if starvation didn't get him first. She felt she'd had no choice. Nor had she been so proud as not to see the advantages it would bring him. This way her Callum would grow up a gentleman with a good education and fine manners.

Except things hadn't turned out that way at all. As a result of Lucy's abduction of him, Callum had been brought up as a farmhand. Since his return home, Kate was desperate to make up to him for all that he had lost.

She'd provided him with security in terms of an apprenticeship at Tyson's shoe factory, had done what she could to improve his education. She'd also tactfully attempted to teach him good manners: how to say 'please' and 'thank you', and to use a knife and fork properly. She'd striven to dampen down the Westmorland accent he'd acquired on the farm, so that he wouldn't feel quite so awkward in company. Was it a crime for her to want her son to enjoy the finer things of life?

Oh, but even if she never succeeded in smoothing off the rough corners, didn't she love the bones of him? Nothing else mattered but that he was home safe and well, with her. He was her boy. Although she couldn't help wishing that it had never happened. If only he hadn't gone missing that day, how different life would have been.

If only – two words that had haunted her for years.

If only she'd taken better care of him, paid more attention to her own child and less to the problems of others. If only she hadn't left him making daisy chains on the lawn while she ran after Eliot simply to win yet an argument over Swainson.

If only she hadn't assumed, when she'd realised he was gone, that Eliot had taken him.

If only she'd searched harder… ignoring the fact that she'd been obsessed with searching for him, had tirelessly scoured the town for weeks, months, years in the end, making herself ill in the process. If she'd seen a child in the street who bore the vaguest resemblance to him, Kate's heart would race and she'd follow him until, realising her error, she would quietly weep.

Worst of all, if only she'd recognised him that day at the market, had remonstrated with the farmer's wife when she'd seen her berating the boy, instead of thinking it was none of her business.

If only she could turn back the clock and make everything come right.

If only!

But she could do none of these things. She could only accept how things were now and learn to live with them. Her heart sang with joy to have Eliot home. Yet seeing her husband attempt to embrace his adopted son, whom he'd loved as his own, and be so rebuffed, filled Kate with sorrow and a deep foreboding.

She took the first opportunity to suggest to Callum that he must be patient. 'Time will gradually resolve this sense of strangeness between the two of you. Eliot does care about you, very much.'

The boy said nothing, merely stared at her in sulky silence as he so often did.

He might be difficult, yet he was her son and she loved him. 'I ask only that you think how strange this must all be for Eliot too, after all he has been through these last years. Give him a chance to settle.'

'And what about me? What about what I've been through?'

'I know, m'cushla. I understand. Trust me, it will all work out in the end. We need to allow ourselves time to get to know each other again, that's all.'

'I dun't want to get to know Lucy again, thanks all t'same.'

'No, no, of course you don't, me darlin'. 'Tis unthinkable!'

And there was another *if only*. If only Kate had called the constabulary when she'd learned of her sister-in-law's despicable crime. Instead Kate had turned her out of the house, thinking that would be shame enough for her snobbish sister-in-law. She hadn't felt that it was her place to call in the police. The aunts would have hated a family scandal, and Eliot wasn't around to make the decision.

Where Lucy had lived since then Kate neither knew nor greatly cared, though from snippets of conversation she'd overheard between the aunts, she rather thought Lucy was now occupying their old home in Heversham. Whatever she'd been doing, wherever she'd been these last two years, now she was back, interfering in their lives as she so loved to do.

Kate could only hope that she no longer had vengeance on her mind.

Now she smiled at Callum. 'I won't ask anything of you that is unreasonable, but I'm trusting you to be man enough to forget the past, to put it behind you and make a fresh start. All right?'

The boy said nothing, merely put his hands in his pockets and slunk away.

–

'I've had a word with him, so I have,' Kate informed Eliot. 'Give him a little time and he'll come round. Isn't he feeling just a bit shy and awkward?'

'He was downright rude, Kate. He shouldn't be allowed to get away with such ill manners.'

'I do realise that but he's sorry. He'll be fine, you'll see. You both need time, to be sure, these things can't be rushed.'

Kate insisted that Eliot rest and recuperate, that he do nothing, that even the business be left to its own devices for a while until he felt fully recovered and ready to take up the reins again.

'And how will it survive meanwhile, may I ask?'

'Toby will look after it, though I'll pop in each morning for an hour or two, while you are sleeping.'

'Toby?'

'Toby Lynch, my foreman, if you remember? Since our two businesses merged, he's been vital to the smooth running of the entire company. I simply couldn't manage without him. He was instrumental in helping me deal with the unions just a year or two back: making a new agreement for a fifty-hour week and one week's paid holiday a year. Oh, and that we pay time and a half for overtime.'

'Whose side is he on?'

Kate laughed. 'Ours, of course. A happy work-force makes for full production. With the war over, there's general concern that there might be a slump, now that orders for army boots have dried up. We do need to talk about the factory, Eliot, but not just yet. First you must rest and get properly fit and well.'

Kate was already turning over plans in her mind for how to counteract this downturn. She was keen to concentrate on the women's market. To produce more stylish shoes, as well as keeping up with the usual riding boots, working boots and classic gentlemen's lines.

Once Eliot was fully recovered from his trauma, she would enjoy discussing these ideas with him. Perhaps a part of her hoped that she wouldn't be entirely put out to grass. She still felt that she had much to contribute, that they could work together as a good team.

Kate enjoyed looking after her husband, fussing over him endlessly, bringing him cushions and cups of tea and insisting Mrs Petty make all his favourite dishes. She bought him a walking stick too, which he absolutely refused to use.

'I can walk perfectly well.'

'Indeed you cannot! Don't be stubborn, Eliot, I can see how that leg pains you. The stick will help until you get your strength back.'

She put it in the rack by the front door but he never used it, and when she remonstrated with him again, telling him he was hobbling like an old man and shouldn't be so damned proud, Eliot snapped at her that he was not an invalid.

And indeed he certainly didn't act like one. He had survived in one piece, at least, was still reasonably young and fit, and evidently still virile.

They were like young lovers again, hardly able to keep apart, constantly touching, sharing secret smiles, casting sidelong glances of agony at each other as the clock on the mantelpiece ticked slowly by, aching to sneak off to bed early but not daring to do so.

Once alone, clothes would be discarded with alacrity, buttons snapped, ribbons torn in their anxiety to touch flesh to flesh. Sometimes Eliot couldn't even wait for her to undress, or to reach the great bed they shared, pulling her into his arms the moment the bedroom door closed, pushing up her skirts and consuming her with his mouth, his body, his great need of her. He would take her up against the door, making it bang and rattle and the brass handle prod her back as he thrust into her. Whatever the servants would think, Kate dare not imagine.

But what better way to deal with the nightmares which seemed to haunt him night after night?

Afterwards they would lie entwined in the big soft bed, sated, replete until morning and then on waking he would pull her to him while she was still half asleep and wake her with fresh loving. Kate would open herself to him gladly, take him within her. Simply to feel the warm weight of his body upon hers was utter bliss. And when the moment of climax came, she'd throw back her arms, gripping the bed-head in her ecstasy, wrap her legs about his waist as if she were a wanton and move with him in an instinctive rhythm, needing to give him all of her love and more. Afterwards, she would weep softly in his arms, overcome by emotion, quite unable to move or think.

Chapter Fourteen

Eliot wasn't certain whether he was awake or asleep, alive or dead. The dream was so real. But then so was the pain, which meant he must still be alive, mustn't it? He'd been thinking of the boy, of his first encounter with his adopted son after all these years, wondering why he didn't feel more disappointed by his rejection, or any rush of thwarted parental love. Did he have any emotion left in him at all, or had it all run dry?

None of this seemed real. Nothing. Not this house, not his family or the business, not even Kate at times. Oh, yes, Kate must surely be a dream, a sweet and lovely mirage. Otherwise, where had she come from? How could she be here?

He was lying in the straw, smelling the unmistakable stink of pigs, mingled with the scent of his own blood, and cordite, wondering where he was and if he really was alive.

Everything had happened so quickly. They'd stopped to rest by an old church, foolishly thinking it might be a safe spot, but destruction had come upon them right out of the blue, out of the blue heavens in fact, dropping like hell-fire on earth, blasting open a crater big enough to lose half an army in, or so it seemed. Certainly more than half of Eliot's men.

'Get down, keep your heads down!' He remembered that much, shouting to them, warning them. He must have done, because everybody did go down, some of them never to come up again.

What was left of his troop must have brought him here, probably because the sty had seemed the warmest, safest place to spend the night. He wasn't sure that the ripe odour didn't outweigh these benefits, but beggars couldn't be choosers. They'd slept in barns, cow sheds, beneath hedges, any place they could lay their heads.

And wherever he was, in some make-shift billet or his dugout, his rabbit hole as he called it, he would dream of Kate's lovely face. He'd conjure it into his mind and feast on it, until the pain of thinking about her became too great to bear.

The pain in his leg was worse. It felt as if some wild animal had sunk its fangs into it and was gnawing the limb off. He could see the festering sore, view it with a curious detachment, aware that the loss of blood was already great and that it showed no sign of stopping. He couldn't allow this to happen. He had to get up and take care of his men. Yet something was pressing him down. He couldn't move, was beginning to feel oddly detached and light-headed, the hole where a long shard of bone poked through seeming to grow larger by the second. Someone had ripped open his trouser leg, or had the shell done that?

There was a tourniquet of sorts; bandages stuffed into the hole. Neither seemed to be very effective as the wound was a mess of black and scarlet, of mud and blood, covered with flies half the time. Had he severed an artery? Was this how death felt: this aching tiredness, this desperate, dark chill?

'Where's the cavalry when you need it?' The voice came out of the darkness, from someone huddled shivering beside him. It was a good question.

'What a place to end yer days,' said another, 'in a sodding pig sty.'

'Aye, but at least we have a roof over our heads. They'll find us soon.'

'Pigs might fly,' came the droll response to this piece of optimism.

'If tha does see any flying pigs, mate, it'll be me, beggaring off up to heaven,' said another.

'Well, we're at least handy for a few bacon butties.'

Eliot had often noticed that the men were at their most flippant and jovial when their backs were against the wall, as now. They'd even named their gun pit Sandbag Villa, situated in Whizz-Bang Lane. Their sense of humour, black though it may be, helped to sustain them. He felt nothing but sympathy and admiration for the fortitude and courage of his men. They were filled with optimism, quite certain they would be the victors in the end.

Morale was high, and it was partly his job, of course, to keep it that way.

He wished he felt half their courage, one fraction of their faith in the future. Instead he felt certain he was failing them. For some reason he was filled with fear, a cold crawling terror stealing away the last of his strength. He knew he mustn't fall asleep, that would be fatal. Somehow he must struggle to keep his eyes open, his mind centred.

He had to get them out of here, except that they were still being heavily shelled, pinned down, unable to move, trapped like flies under a jar.

A great weight was pressing down on him. Was it the enemy? Were they being attacked again? Eliot tried to push the sensation away, to rise and fight back, shouting at his men to '*Move, move, move!*' He woke on a scream, with Kate ashen-faced beside him.

—

If life with Callum was difficult, Eliot proved to present greater problems for Kate. But then how could she expect him simply to settle back into domestic bliss after the terrible experiences of war?

He seemed to find it difficult to concentrate, and showed not the slightest interest in the factory, or in his painting which had once so absorbed him. He would either sit in morose silence for hour upon hour or else be frenetically dashing about, insisting she leave whatever she was doing and they go out for a ride, or a walk, or to visit old friends. At once, this minute. He couldn't seem to keep still for a moment, even though, more often than not, his actions showed no real sense of purpose.

She tried to get him interested in his beloved garden, but he seemed to have lost all his old passion for that too.

'Do you remember planting these trees, saying how they would be here for our son, long after we were dust?'

Eliot gazed upon them as if they meant nothing at all to him.

Even the rose garden, where he'd loved to walk and kiss her under the arbour, didn't inspire him now. Where once he had known the name of every rose and never could pass one by without snipping off a dead head or drawing in the scent of a bloom, now he seemed oblivious to their charms.

Kate had employed a young lad to assist Eliot in what she hoped would be a rejuvenation of both himself and his precious garden, but whenever Tom asked Eliot what needed to be done, her husband would mumble something then walk away in the middle of a sentence. It was all very worrying.

Kate couldn't begin to imagine what he had been through, what horrors he'd seen.

When he woke from one of his regular nightmares she would stroke his head, the tight hardness of his belly, and he would turn to her, taking her fiercely as if to banish the devils that haunted him.

He never spoke of the horrors, though she begged him to do so, hoping it might help to purge his mind in some way. He spoke only of practical matters, of their routine. And if he felt the need to talk, she would hold him in her arms, keep silent and listen, as now.

'We worked in groups of three – one to stand guard, one to clean up the trench while the third took a nap. We maybe got one hour's sleep out of three. Standing on the fire-step was the worst, watching and waiting, seeing nothing but the occasional flare, hearing only the odd explosion. It was the most boring job in the world, taxing the nerves to the limits, for if you let down your guard for a moment, it could be your last. You needed to be quick to spot whatever the enemy was throwing at you, so you could make a speedy evacuation of the trench if necessary. Besides which, falling asleep on duty was a crime for which a soldier could be shot.

'Jesus, Mary and Joseph, *shot*? Simply for falling asleep?'

'War isn't a game, Kate. Men could die as a result of such negligence.'

Not that Eliot would allow that to happen to any of his own men. He'd been tough, but always made certain that those under his command were suitably camouflaged from aerial observation as German planes came over, often just when they were about to go to the battery to eat so that their dinners would be cold and unpalatable by the time the raid was over.

'Will Callum ever forgive me for losing him?' he asked.

'You didn't lose him, he was stolen. It wasn't our fault. He will see that in the end. He's just a boy. Give him time. He doesn't understand.'

'I had boys under my command. Almost as young as Callum is now, far too young to be facing what they were forced to endure, day after day. Yet they did their duty, usually without complaint. Will he ever accept me as a father, Kate, will he?'

'I'm sure he will, if we're patient.'

'Who was that boy we were talking to this morning?'

'That was Tom, the new gardener.'

'Why isn't he in the army?'

'The war is over, Eliot. Tom has been spared from joining up.'

'I prefer Askew. When is Askew coming back? He isn't retired is he? He said he never would retire, loved the garden too much.'

'Askew is dead, my darling. You remember he died right at the beginning of the war?'

'Did he? I forget. Could we have salmon for tea today? I love salmon.'

This was how his conversations went, darting from one subject to the next with neither rhyme nor reason.

He drew her closer to him, a slight smile curving his mouth into a softer line. 'Mealtimes were the only thing we had to look forward to, apart from the delivery of the post when I'd look for your letters. For breakfast we'd get an ounce of cold ham with maybe three-quarters of a cup of lukewarm tea. A bit of bread if we were lucky. Otherwise there were biscuits. Hard and tasteless though they might be, they were still welcome, particularly with a little cheese, even if it had probably gone mouldy. And we got any amount of jam. I'm quite sure that the war was won on jam butties and bully beef.'

And he laughed then, as if it were all some sort of joke, and Kate laughed with him. It was either that, or cry.

–

One of their favourite walks that summer was over Scout Scar, a soft Lakeland breeze taking the heat out of the beautiful June days. Rock roses grew in the crevices amongst the limestone and Kate could detect the sweet scents of lily-of-the-valley, saxifrage and columbine.

On this particular afternoon Eliot laid her gently down in the long grass between the juniper bushes, making love to her as if she were a maid and he a mere boy. Crazy with love, oblivious of their middle-class, middle-aged, respectable station in life, they giggled at their daring, dozed and kissed, then loved again.

The auld grey town of Kendal was spread out in the valley below them, their town, their kingdom, and they felt as free as the clean Lakeland air buffeting their naked bodies, free to enjoy life and the glorious prospect of a brand new tomorrow.

'Have you thought about the future?' she asked, when she could draw breath. 'I have so many ideas I'd like to share with you, when you're ready.'

He smiled at her fondly, caressing the silk of her skin, her wayward, abundant hair. 'You wouldn't be my Kate if you didn't have something to say on the subject.'

'It might make you feel better to start thinking about the future, stop you looking back into the past quite so much. Might even help to prevent the nightmares if you had something new and positive to think about, and plan for.'

'I will, I will. When the time is right, I shall at least agree to listen.'

But she couldn't wait for some unforeseen time in the future. Kate was bursting with impatience, needing to talk about it now, wanting to hasten his recovery and believing work was the answer, as it had been for her when at her lowest. 'I thought I might like to open a shop.'

'A shop?' Eliot looked startled, laughed, as if she had said something amusing. 'What sort of shop, dearest?'

'A shoe shop, of course, what else? Don't you think that would be a grand idea? It would be stocked exclusively with Tyson's shoes, naturally. I would specialise in ladies' shoes, at least to begin with, and children's perhaps. Different styles and fittings. Lots to choose from. It would be bright and clean and very fashionable. A place a lady could feel comfortable in, not one of these dull, dusty shops nobody wants to go into.'

Her husband lay back with a sigh and closed his eyes, was silent for so long that Kate began to wonder if he had fallen asleep. In that moment, while she waited impatiently for his response, she realised how desperately important it was to her for him to agree, for Eliot to be as excited by the idea as she was. But perhaps she shouldn't have mentioned it quite yet. Perhaps that had been a mistake. It was too soon. She should have waited a while longer.

He sat up suddenly and looked about him, rubbing his eyes as if he really had been asleep. 'Time we were going I expect. Mrs Petty will shoot us if we are late for lunch.' He got to his feet, holding out his hand to help her up. But Kate hesitated, had to persist. She simply couldn't keep quiet.

'And the shop?'

'What?'

'The shoe shop. Do you think it's a good idea?'

Frowning slightly, he looked bemused for a moment and then his brow cleared and he laughed again. 'Oh, that. I've told you, not yet, my darling. I can't put my mind to business matters just yet.'

'But we must do something, now that we no longer have the orders for army boots.'

'Later, my dear. Much, much later. Stop worrying about it. Right now I simply want to look at you, to know that I exist, that I'm free to enjoy you, enjoy life.'

And enjoy her he did. Eliot took her whenever and wherever he wished. In the stables when he was harnessing the horses ready to ride out in the carriage and young Tom could have walked in at any moment. On the kitchen table one night when she went down to get herself a glass of milk; in the summer house over afternoon tea; another time in the rose garden. And when the aunts came innocently upon them, Kate was mightily flustered to be found with her hair like a bird's nest, her bodice unfastened and the familiar tell-tale flush upon her apple cheeks. Not that the two maiden ladies gave any indication that they had noticed her disarray, they were far too well-mannered.

For all her concern over her husband's health, those first weeks of his homecoming were idyllic, so very precious.

So it came as a shock to Kate when, one morning some weeks later, their citadel of happiness came tumbling down.

Chapter Fifteen

From the moment of his safe return, Kate had been at pains to include Callum in absolutely every part of her life. He had missed out on so much through his childhood years, on all the opportunities she had wanted for him, but Kate was determined that his future at least would be secure and bright. Anxious for him to have a trade at his fingertips, she'd apprenticed him to one of Tyson's most skilled shoemakers, and he was doing well. Callum was methodical and painstaking, his fingers agile and supple, his strong shoulders able to bear the physically demanding job.

While living and working outdoors on the farm in the Langdales for most of his youth, he'd had little or no education and one day had confessed to his mother that he could not read. Kate had vowed to teach him, assuring him that it wasn't too late to learn. Callum was sensitive on the subject, feeling deep shame over this inadequacy on his part, and the lessons were carried out behind closed doors in the study, in private, never openly referred to in front of the family.

He had proved to be bright and intelligent, and even though he came to book learning relatively late in life, was making good progress. But finding books simple enough for him to read while still being suitable for a sixteen-year-old boy was well-nigh impossible. Kate had settled on classic adventure tales for him, which he loved: *Arabian Nights*, *The Tales of King Arthur* perhaps, or *Around the World in Eighty Days*. These interludes of reading aloud became their favourite time of the day as it gave each the chance to get to know the other a little better. Every evening after Kate had watched and corrected as her son painstakingly spelled out words or did a few sums to practise his arithmetic, she would then read a little from a favourite book, Callum following the words along with her.

They were thus engaged one evening when Eliot walked in upon them. Kate had believed him to be taking a nap before dinner, and was startled by the sudden interruption. Callum leaped to his feet, his cheeks growing scarlet as if he were guilty of some crime.

Eliot frowned, then marching over, picked up the book and gave a snort of derision. 'What's this? *Robinson Crusoe*? Good Lord, not still needing your mother to read to you, boy, before you go to bed? Do you suck a dummy too?'

Kate, appalled by his insensitivity, was on her feet in a second, her hand reaching out to snatch the book from his grasp. 'Eliot! That is most dreadfully unkind. Cannot mother and son enjoy a few quiet moments together? Isn't this the only chance we get to be together in a busy day?'

That too was a mistake, apparently. Her husband glowered. 'If you are implying that I'm not pulling my weight, then perhaps you're right. It clearly is time I did some useful work. As should this boy of yours, by the looks of it, if he still clings to his mother's apron strings. My boys didn't have stories read to them at bedtime – they lay listening to whizz-bangs, thinking they might have their heads blown off at any minute.'

'That's hardly my fault, sir,' Callum said, his face white as parchment.

'Indeed not, but your freedom to read these pretty yarns is largely due to their sacrifice. Think on that.'

Without another word, the boy walked from the room.

Kate ran after him. 'Callum, don't go!' But he paid no attention and she knew instinctively, in that moment, that he would never come near the study for reading lessons again. It felt as if all her hard work to make up to her son for the years of neglect had been thrown back in her face. She was furious.

The moment the door closed she turned on Eliot. 'Why did you have to be so damned high-handed? Can't you see I'm trying to help him, give him some of the education he missed? And you march in here like some commanding officer inspecting his troops and bark orders at him. How dare you! Do you not realise the courage it took for him to admit to me that he couldn't read, and wasn't he doing grand?'

Eliot was taken aback by her vehement attack and had the grace to look a little sheepish. 'I meant no harm. I didn't think… didn't realise.'

'Then you *should* think. You should consider other people occasionally. Callum may not have suffered the war as your "boys" did, but nor has he enjoyed a stable, safe childhood with loving parents and a good education. Doesn't he at least deserve some of that now? Thanks to your vindictive sister-in-law, he was denied the opportunity.'

Quite unexpectedly, Eliot dismissed her comment with a casual shake of the head, 'I'm sorry, Kate, but I can give little credence to this tale of Callum's so-called abduction.'

She looked at him in astonishment. 'Are you saying that I'm making it all up, that I'm lying? Or perhaps that Callum is?' Kate appreciated that Eliot was deeply hurt by the boy's obstructive attitude, but not this. Not for one moment had she expected him to disbelieve her.

'I'm saying that a resentful adolescent is not a reliable source of evidence. Maybe he's always been lazy, didn't want to learn, and is now taking advantage of your soft heart, your sense of maternal guilt, to wheedle his way back in and have an easy life.'

'*What*? It hasn't been at all easy for him living here. And isn't the boy desperate to learn, thirsty for knowledge and information? He's making good progress. Or at least he was, until you barged in playing the sergeant-major.'

Eliot ignored her, unused to having his will challenged, his mind for once entirely focused on his argument. 'Was anyone else witness to this heinous act Lucy purportedly carried out?'

'Of course not, how could there be any witness? She did it in secret, cleverly covering up her tracks, but she most definitely *did* do it. She abducted my child!'

'Our child. You will keep forgetting the small matter of the adoption.'

'Don't split hairs, Eliot. Lucy *stole* him.'

'And you know this for certain because Callum says so?'

Kate was stunned by his disbelieving attitude. 'Yes, I do. 'Tis so. 'Tis the truth!'

He patted her shoulder, as if she were some foolish little woman who needed things explaining properly. 'I can well understand, my darling, how upset you must have been when he told this tale, but I ask you to consider what proof do you actually have? None. Only the word of a mixed-up boy who feels a natural resentment against the parents who allowed him to wander off and get lost. Any child would in the circumstances. In consequence, he has been allowed to stand as judge and jury against his own aunt. No wonder Lucy feels a deep resentment over being cast out from the family and her home.'

'*Lucy* feels resentment? She told you that, did she?'

'She did, over lunch at the County, the day of my return. She is at a loss to understand your behaviour. Her feelings have been deeply hurt, her life well-nigh ruined.'

'*Her* life has been ruined!' Kate felt her knees go all weak and wobbly, a sick feeling lodge itself in her stomach. She longed to sink into a chair but somehow remained standing rigid before him, determined to prove her case. 'And what about *my* feelings? And *Callum's* life? Who ruined that? *Lucy!*'

'So you say. Or rather, so Callum says.'

'And you'd take her word against mine?'

'I might well take her word against a vindictive adolescent's. The matter needs to be carefully investigated before I can properly decide.'

'Investigated?'

Instinctively Kate had known that Eliot would see no wrong in his sister-in-law, or that he would forgive her if he did. Didn't he always see the best in people? He was far too soft-hearted for his own good. He'd been exactly the same over that conniving foreman, Swainson. He was the most incredibly stubborn, obstinately fair-minded man.

Concern about his reaction had been behind her decision not to call in the police the day she'd discovered the truth, knowing that Eliot would do anything, believe anything rather than disturb the smooth running of his life, or face a family scandal.

Yet he *must* face the truth. She couldn't have him implying that her son was a liar.

'What about Flora, is she a liar too? The day Callum returned home, Lucy had promised to pick her up from school, but Flora says that her aunt wasn't there waiting for her as she usually was. Lucy arrived late and scolded Flora because she wasn't standing by the school gate. The child was going frantic, so she was, looking everywhere for her aunt. Then, Flora says, Lucy seemed to lose control and began to beat her about the head, slapped and punched her and left her for dead up an alley. Sure and Flora might well have died had not Callum found her and brought her home, black with bruises and covered in mud. Lucy had done that to her.'

'Did she say so? Did Lucy admit to having beaten the child?'

'No, of course she didn't!'

'Did Flora say her aunt had done this heinous thing?'

'Yes, I'm telling you, she did.'

'And Flora came home with Callum? Quite out of the blue, our long-lost son turned up at this opportune moment?'

Kate hesitated fractionally before answering this question, her temper cooling a little. 'Y-yes, Callum found her lying unconscious in the alleyway.'

'What a remarkable coincidence.'

'Not so. Callum was attending Kendal market that day with Mrs Brocklebank, and sneaked off

201

to walk by the river. He recognised the house and knocked on the door. Apparently Ida caught a glimpse of him when she was in the hall, though she hadn't the first idea who he was. Lucy sent him packing, which she would do, of course. She'd recognised him instantly, and no doubt took out her fury on Flora.'

'How do you know Callum wasn't the perpetrator of this crime, that *he* wasn't the one to beat up Flora?'

'Utter rubbish. He doesn't have it in him to beat anyone up. He's a very gentle boy.'

'You are his mother, you'd be bound to think so.'

'And why would he do such a thing?'

'Out of jealousy because Flora was still at home being petted and loved, and he, the outsider, was lost and forgotten.'

Kate could feel all the blood draining from her face, from every limb, despite her heart pumping like a mad thing. 'That's not true. Callum adores Flora. To be sure he'd never hurt her, and they met once before remember, at the market.'

'When he learned who she was, and started to plan his revenge.'

Kate was shocked yet again by his twisted interpretation of events. 'No, that's not the way of it at all. Flora told me it wasn't the first time Lucy had hurt her.'

'She'd be bound to say that, wouldn't she?' Eliot scoffed.

'Why would she? Why would she protect Callum, a stranger to her at that time? Flora was systematically abused over a long period, and I was too damned busy with the factory and with my own army boots business even to notice. How do you think that makes me feel?'

'Perhaps it was merely Flora's way of getting your attention?'

Kate stared at him, speechless for a long moment, quite unable to believe they were even having this argument. 'If you don't believe me, why don't you ask her?'

'I certainly will ask her. We'll get this matter cleared up once and for all, see what Flora and Callum have to say for themselves. But Lucy too should be allowed the chance to speak up on her own behalf. That is only fair and just.'

'For goodness' sake, Eliot, you're talking as if you were about to hold a court martial. These are your children we are speaking of here.'

'Nevertheless, we will conduct this investigation with all due propriety, honour and integrity. Lucy must be given the opportunity to put her case.'

Chapter Sixteen

Eliot chose to conduct the investigation with everyone present, as if they were young soldiers being called to account in front of their commanding officer. Callum and Flora looking distinctly nervous, the aunts sat huddled close together against the tapestry cushions, their faces mirroring their bemusement and dismay. Today they wore their usual black, Cissie having removed her doggie-scented cardigan in honour of the occasion. Vera still wore a fichu of lace at her throat, although it had been considered outmoded even before the war. Aunt Vera's short cropped hair was more of a muddy grey these days than the rich brown it used to be, if every bit as neat and tidy. Cissie, sadly, had never been tidy in her life.

It was all unspeakably awful. Kate strongly protested against this so-called investigation, hating the notion of seeing her children put under such close scrutiny before an audience, let alone the very idea of having to entertain Lucy in her own front parlour. She told Eliot as much.

'This is not the right way to tackle such a sensitive issue. Please, speak to each child alone first. In complete privacy.'

'We must not only be fair, but be seen to be fair.'

'This is not a court martial, Eliot.'

'I am aware of that. Nonetheless, justice must be seen to be done.'

'These are our children, not some of your men. This isn't the war.'

Eliot half wished that it was. In some ways he'd almost enjoyed the war, relishing the company of his men. And then a bomb had destroyed most of the little church in which they were hiding, burying so many of them in stone and soil. He could remember seeing the ground pitted with holes. He was in one of them, grinding sand between his teeth, desperately fighting for air as he clawed his way to the surface. Some of the men were running, their cries of fear vying with the scream of heavy shelling all around. He'd got up to run with them but found he couldn't.

Yet he'd been thankful still to have his leg, for all he knew that it was broken. Had it not been for the quick thinking of his sergeant, who'd dragged him away from the strafing, the rest of him would have been riddled with bullets too.

He would never forget the horror of that moment. Dead men lying all around like rag dolls, one young face staring right at him, eyes wide open, sightless.

Moments before they'd been joking together, the boy planning how he would propose to his girl-friend, how many sons they might have. Now there was no response from the would-be bridegroom. Another soldier had risen on one knee, as if he'd just been about to get up and leave, but hadn't quite made it.

They buried them later, all of those fine young men. Eliot remembered propping himself against a tree, grating out a few words from some prayer or other through a dry throat, choking with the dust and ash of death, of destruction.

But one had run away, had deserted. He'd been brought back, of course, and dealt with as all cowards are. Put in front of a firing squad. Eliot himself had given the order with not a scrap of pity in his heart. How could there be?

He turned to Kate now, trying to make her understand. 'You may have heard their side of the story, but I have not. I need to hear it from their own lips before I can judge its credibility. Whether they are heroes or lying cowards. And it is long past time to allow Lucy also to put her case.'

'Heroes or...? Eliot, I...'

'Enough. Ask Lucy to come in, Aunt Vera, if you please.'

And so she came, flouncing into the house from which she'd been banned with a smile of pure triumph on her beautiful face, violet eyes sparkling as if she'd already won a victory. As indeed she had, simply by being invited to step over the threshold.

Kate was forced ruefully to admit that her sister-in-law still looked marvellous despite her more matronly appearance these days, her plump breasts straining against the burgundy silk of her gown which was a work of art in itself with all its draped layers, tucks, pleats and folds. The colour set off the glossy jet of her hair, swept up beneath the silliest of hats which bore the tallest possible feather. Even her parasol was much frilled and beribboned. Not for Lucy the current fashion for simplicity and clean lines, although how she found the money to be so elegantly gowned and so immaculately coiffured, Kate could not imagine.

Ever since she'd been widowed when her husband Charles had taken his own life because of insurmountable debts, she'd been supported by his brother Eliot and Tyson's Shoes. Kate herself had been responsible for ensuring Lucy's very generous allowance was punctiliously paid each and every month while Eliot was away at war. It was meant to permit her to live in comfort, covering necessities such as rent, food and general living expenses. But it surely did not run to the kind of elegant clothes Lucy chose to wear, nor to keeping the French maid she insisted on having.

Kate didn't care to think what debts her sister-in-law had already acquired, or who would be responsible for paying them off.

She said nothing now as Lucy settled herself in the wing-backed chair set between the two sofas. She was almost purring with self-satisfaction, smiling at everyone around her with the kind of serenity that spoke of supreme confidence in her own feminine ability to manipulate a situation to her advantage. Lucy certainly did not give the impression of a woman shamed, a woman with something to fear. Kate felt chilled to the bone just watching her.

'It feels so lovely to be home again,' she simpered. 'Though I'm not quite sure what the occasion is, or why I've been summoned.'

Kate bit back the comment which sprang instantly to her lips, that Tyson Lodge was no longer Lucy's home. But how could she say such a thing now that the master himself had returned and was the one who'd invited Lucy here? Kate glanced up into Eliot's face, carefully shuttered and inscrutable, and then across at her son.

Callum had adopted his favourite position, propped against the mantelpiece. Flora was seated on the corner of the sofa nearest to him, her fingers nervously pleating the fabric of her frock.

Neither so much as glanced in Lucy's direction and Kate's heart went out to them both. Something inside her seemed to swell with outrage at seeing her own children so cowed, so swamped in misery.

Eliot cleared his throat, looking very much the commanding officer about to issue a damning indictment upon his troops. But his eyes, Kate noticed, did not appear to be entirely focused, as if his thoughts were elsewhere.

They were fixed somewhere in the past. He'd seen dreadful things: limbs blown off, holes punched into his men. When would the sick feeling leave his belly? When did one grow accustomed to senseless slaughter? He doubted one ever did. No wonder his boys had sometimes lost heart, but cowards had to be winkled out and dealt with. There was no room in a war for lead-swingers and liars, for those incapable of taking responsibility for their own actions, their own failures.

He had always taken his own responsibilities seriously, very seriously indeed, for the sake of the well-being and safety of the entire company. And as it was in the army, so it would be in civilian life. The same standards must apply.

'We'll deal with Callum last. Flora, come here, child.'

Without having planned to do so, Kate found she was on her feet. 'This outrage has gone on long enough! Sure and you cannot expect my children to speak freely while Lucy is present. It's intolerable. An abomination. Utterly unfair, so it is.'

Eliot came and put a hand on her shoulder and gently pushed her back down in her seat. 'Maternal hysteria will assist no one, Kate. Let us all remain calm, shall we? I'm sure this entire business is no more than a trivial misunderstanding which can easily be cleared up.'

'Trivial misunderstanding? I don't believe what I'm hearing, why I…'

'Kate, please. Do attempt to remain calm in front of the children.'

And Kate was forced to subside, as if she were the guilty party.

Flora was staring up at her father in startled dismay. She had Kate's fair complexion, lightly freckled, but Eliot's gloriously dark, chestnut-brown eyes to match her dark brown, wavy hair, marking her out as a Tyson from the moment of her birth. No milksop baby blue for her. A pert chin and snub nose now showed her as a beauty in the making for all her schoolgirl, leggy awkwardness. Flora got up from her seat and stepped forward in answer to his summons and stood before her father, her gaze fixed on the toes of her shiny buttoned shoes.

'Tell me truthfully, Flora. Did your aunt here, who apparently cared for you while your mother was working hard, running both businesses because I was away at the war, ever do anything deliberately to hurt you? Come, you can speak freely. Tell me the truth.'

Flora cast a quick, sideways glance across at her mother and Kate was up again in a flash, aching to rush to her side. Only the condemning light in Eliot's eyes and Aunt Vera's hand on her elbow, persuaded her to sit down again. Nevertheless, she persisted in making her point. 'How can she speak the truth with Lucy sitting there?'

'Please do not interrupt again, Kate, or I will have to ask you to leave the room. This tribunal – er – investigation, must be conducted fairly and properly.'

He could still hear the sounds of gunfire and bombing popping and cracking in his head, the sound of men screaming for their mothers. He could name every shell. Besides the whizz-bangs, so called for obvious reasons, there were sling bombs; hand grenades; trench mortars: the most deadly of all, and even oil cans filled with high explosives and any rubbish the enemy could pack into them. The entire area had been pitted with dugouts linked together by the infamous trenches, running with water and infested with vermin, so that your feet rotted where you stood, assuming the rats didn't gnaw your toes off first.

This house, this genteel life his womenfolk had lead in it while he was away dealing with all of that, even Callum's bare existence in the farm in the Langdales, was paradise by comparison.

'Flora has nothing to fear. I am her papa and will take good care of her. I am a man of honour and integrity, and expect any child of mine to be likewise. It is required of every Tyson, bred in us from birth.'

Kate felt herself shrink, knowing she came from no such grand family, that honour was something she and Dermot had never even considered, survival being everything to them.

'Now speak up, child. Has your aunt Lucy ever lifted a finger to hurt you? No, no, do not look at your mama, look at me. Tell me truly. Has she?'

Flora heard the rustle of her aunt's dress, could smell the over-powering perfume she wore which brought back so many painful childhood memories: nightmares even. Of being pinched on her tummy and smacked very hard on her bottom, of being made to march backwards and forwards with her arms raised, of being left out in the rain, forced to eat eggs which she hated and made her ill.

She'd tried once to explain her misery to Kate but her mother either hadn't understood or didn't believe her, telling her to be a brave little soldier, that they all had to do their bit. Adults never believed a word you said. Only Callum had ever truly understood, but then he had good reason.

The silence seemed to go on interminably, and then it was broken. By Lucy herself.

'Of course she will say that I smacked her. All children need discipline from time to time, and she was subject to the most dreadful tantrums. Kate spoiled her, you see, out of guilt for leaving the child to her own devices while she took on your role, Eliot. Understandable perhaps, for the situation was extremely difficult, as you will appreciate.'

She sounded so reasonable, so calm. Kate could feel herself start to shake, itched to run to Flora and gather her darling child in her arms, but Eliot's hand was once again firmly pressing down upon her shoulder.

'I appreciate how difficult it must have been for you, Lucy. Indeed, we all suffered in our various ways, some more than others. Well now, Flora. Is this true? Did you have tantrums? Answer me now.'

Tears were rolling down Flora's cheeks. It was as if she were back there in her room and Aunt Lucy was telling her to get dressed, or undressed, or make up her bed, and the buttons wouldn't work in her small chubby fingers, or the sheets kept slipping off the bed, and every time she failed to obey an instruction, a ringing slap would strike her. The same words she heard so often then seemed to echo in her mind now.

'You are so very naughty, no wonder your mammy neglects you and doesn't love you any more. You are going to have to learn better manners, or nobody will love you ever again.'

Flora whimpered even now at the memory. 'No,' she mumbled, her voice barely above a tremulous whisper.

'What did you say, child?' Eliot persisted. 'Speak up so that we can all hear you.'

'No. She didn't touch me.'

'There you are,' said Lucy with great satisfaction. 'Didn't I tell you!'

Chapter Seventeen

The remainder of the investigation seemed very much a foregone conclusion. Callum was treated to a similar grilling to Flora, called upon to explain himself and present evidence of his claim against his aunt. Of course, the poor boy had none, other than a young child's sketchy recollections of a traumatic incident.

Lucy wept a good deal, sighing and dabbing at her eyes with a lace-trimmed handkerchief, throwing agonised looks at Eliot in an overt plea for sympathy. It was, Kate had to admit, a skilled and polished performance.

'So you have no real evidence. Neither the Brocklebanks nor the Union Workhouse can name the person who brought you to them that day?'

'No,' Callum mumbled.

'It could quite easily have been some right-thinking person who found you, a small boy of five at the time, wandering alone in the streets.'

'It was Lucy.'

'You *think* it was Lucy, but you have no real proof that it was. Isn't that correct?'

Silence.

'It could very easily have been another lady, who was simply trying to be kind.'

Callum's face was tight with anger. 'It were her.'

'You were known throughout that period as Allan?'

'Aye.'

'But if Lucy herself had taken you, why would she give the wrong name?'

'To cover her tracks. And she beat me, just as she did Flora.'

'We have already heard from Flora herself that Lucy never touched her. I put it to you that you told Flora to accuse her aunt of causing the bruises that day, to deflect the real blame from yourself.'

'That's not true!'

'Tell me, boy, why exactly did your aunt abduct you and apparently put you in the Union work-house? For what purpose? What did she hope to gain by such a cruel act?'

At this point, Kate felt unable to keep quiet any longer. 'I think I can explain that point. She did it out of revenge. Callum had usurped the place of her own children in your affections, robbing them of their inheritance, as she saw it.'

For a second Eliot appeared discomfited and confused, a frown creasing his brow as he attempted to sift through the fog of his memory. Had he disinherited Lucy's children? He really didn't think so. But when had he last adjusted his will? Was it after Callum went missing, or before? It was all so long ago he couldn't quite remember. So much had happened since.

His leg was throbbing from standing on it for so long this morning and he longed to sit down and relax. He'd take a glass or two of whisky perhaps with his lunch, to numb the pain.

Pain. It was a small price to pay for his life.

The Medical Corps must have come to stretcher him out, risking their own lives in the process, for he'd found himself in a hospital ward. At least, he'd thought that's what it was. It turned out to be a clearing station for the wounded, little more than a huge tent, eerily dark and as close to hell as you could get without actually going there.

He brought himself back to the present with a jerk and glared at the boy in front of him, for a moment struggling to put a name to him, to remind himself of the object of this enquiry.

Ah, yes, lies and possible cowardice. The boy was blaming Lucy for his own childish foolishness, and naturally Kate was supporting him, looking for any motive Lucy might have, however unlikely. This was beginning to sound more and more like a tale in a penny dreadful.

The odour of death had been everywhere, that sickly sweet stink of rotting flesh, not quite disguised by an overlay of carbolic soap. There were sobs and moans and sounds of crying all around him; the injured being carried back and forth on stretchers, some with red tags on their feet, labelling them as not worth trying to save.

'Eliot?'

Kate's voice was coming through the mists of memory. Eliot mentally shook himself. He focused upon her lovely face with difficulty.

'I might have disapproved of Lucy's predilection for over-spending but I've always made a point of providing for her and her children ever since my brother died. And she was well aware that I would continue to do so, although obviously the factory would go to Callum, my adopted son, in the fullness of time. Lucy was aware of that too. Were you not, sister-in-law?'

'Of course, who else?' Lucy replied, with saccharine sweetness.

Eliot rubbed his leg, tried to ease it into a more comfortable position.

They'd needed to operate on it right away, to save it. Just before he began, the doctor had told him that he'd run out of anaesthetic. The agony of those long, pain-wracked hours on the operating table would be carved forever in Eliot's mind, although it probably didn't take anything like that long. He was one of dozens dealt with that day.

'Isn't the truth of the matter, Callum, that it was all some sort of silly prank, childish naughtiness that went wrong? You ran away because no one was paying you any attention that day, and in the way of all children who get lost, you blamed us, your parents, for losing you, and worse, for not finding you.'

'No.'

'Now you've latched on to Lucy here as a convenient scapegoat, because if she had carried out this heinous crime, we again would have to share some part of the blame because we never noticed her involvement. In fact, you'd rather anyone took the blame for those missing years than yourself. You are simply a cowardly boy, an adolescent filled with resentment, isn't that the truth of it?'

'*No!*' Callum almost shouted his reply this time.

By some stroke of good fortune, or medical skill, Eliot had managed to avoid infection and lived to tell the tale. But he would never forget the screams of those who didn't survive, the blinded men begging for water, the horrific burns, the missing limbs and the disfigurement of his comrades. No room in that tent for cowards. This boy didn't know how lucky he was to have escaped all of that.

Eliot had made up his mind. 'I think we've heard enough.'

Lucy was exonerated and was to be allowed to move back into Tyson Lodge.

Flora hid away in her room, refusing absolutely to come downstairs and welcome her aunt, no matter how much Eliot might exhort her to do so. Callum too was noticeable by his absence.

The little girl was distraught, sobbing that her darling papa did not believe a word she'd said. Kate cuddled and reassured her, trying to explain how her papa was not quite himself; that later, when he'd had time to consider the matter more closely, he would surely change his mind.

He certainly would if Kate had anything to do with it. Not for one moment would she risk allowing that woman anywhere near her children in future. 'He'll come round to believing you, sweetie, I promise.'

'But it'll be too late then, won't it, Mammy? Lucy will already be here.' Flora's big brown eyes gazed at her in deep distress and Kate's heart clenched. How was she going to protect her child?

'Sure and she'll not lay a finger on you, not with Daddy and Mammy both here. She wouldn't dare. You're quite safe, my angel, don't you fret. Now why don't we put some rags in your hair, then you'll have ringlets in the morning? Make you look even prettier, shall we, my darling?'

But Flora shook her head, not in the mood to be pacified by such blandishments. It took some time, and at least two stories being read to her from her favourite *Hans Christian Andersen Storybook*, before Flora settled for the night.

Concerned that the outcome of this uncalled-for investigation would only make Callum's resentment against his father worse, Kate hurried along to her son's room. Finding it empty, she frantically searched the entire house and gardens, finally locating him in the summer house at the furthest end beyond the rose garden. It was the sound of sobbing which alerted her some moments before she reached him. Kate hung back, hoping it would cease, not wishing to embarrass her proud, sixteen-year-old boy.

When the sound had eased to quiet sniffles, she called out his name. 'Callum, is that you? Are you there, m'darlin'?' By the time she reached him, he appeared quite composed, his dignity intact.

Kate put her arms about her son and hugged him tight. 'Wasn't that the most dreadful thing? You mustn't blame your papa too much, m'cushla. Hasn't he had a worse time in the army than we'll ever know or appreciate? I'll talk to him, so I will. Make him understand.'

'He never will.' Callum carefully extricated himself from her embrace, embarrassed by this display of motherly affection.

'He will so, given time. Not everything can be solved in the blink of an eye, not in this world. We need patience, to be sure. Won't Lucy condemn herself, given time? No, no, don't look alarmed, I don't mean I'll let her harm either one of you, ever again. I mean, simply by her own difficult, selfish behaviour. Won't he soon remember how very mean and manipulative she can be? We only have to watch and wait, and he'll soon come to see the truth, mark my words. Now will ye walk yer mam back to the house and I'll make us both a mug of hot cocoa?'

'I'm not a child, Mother, to be mollified by such treats.'

Kate looked at her over-serious son with deep love reflected in her gaze. 'Don't I know it? And wasn't I robbed of all those precious years, just as you were robbed of your childhood? We can never get that time back but we must make sure that the future remains bright. We must make very sure of that.'

Kate couldn't bear even to consider how such a decision might affect Callum and Flora. From now on, for the rest of her life perhaps, she would have to be vigilant in protecting them.

–

Lucy came the very next morning, rolling up in her new motor which was piled high with her personal treasures, pictures, vases, *objets d'art* and a fine set of Moroccan leather luggage, not forgetting the French maid, just as if she owned the place.

Mrs Petty, the cook-housekeeper, was heard to remark to Ida that it was as if they'd been struck by a hurricane, and the entire household had got caught up in the blast.

'I've never stopped since first light. That one could make a donkey run.'

Ida, who hadn't risen much beyond skivvy in all the twenty years she'd worked at Tyson Lodge, nodded in agreement that she likewise hadn't sat down all day either. Even so, she scurried about the kitchen, tidying things away, slicing bread, pork and pickle for Mrs Petty's late lunch, pouring boiling water into a bowl with a measure of cold, well laced with mustard which Mrs Petty swore was a sure cure for her bunions.

'Hurry up, Ida, me poor feet are fair killing me. By heck, but we've seen it all in this house. Such comings and goings we've had.' With a deep sigh of relief she sank her feet into the near scalding water, tucking up her skirts to reveal a pair of fat knees encased in pale pink Directoire knickers.

'From the day Kate O'Connor arrived in her mucky boots and handed over that starving brat of hers for adoption, everything has been out of kilter in this household. And poor Madam, poor sweet Amelia, dying like that, thinking she was having a child of her own at last, when really she was suffering from a terrible tumour! Since her death we've had the abduction, the aunts descending upon us like a pair of meddling old crows, an illegitimate daughter, and the shock of the master marrying the nursemaid, our lovely Kate as she now is: the girl from Poor House Lane as she then was. Lord save us, what a pantomime!'

'Don't forget the war an' all,' said Ida, wanting to add her own two pennyworth to this litany of disaster.

'Yer right, lass. Even the bleeding Hun had to stick his oar in. What we've suffered! Hurry up with that cuppa, I'm fair clemmed. And I'll have a piece of that shortbread an' all.'

'Right, Mrs Petty. And a slice of the fruit loaf to go with it?'

'Aye, just to keep it company, why not? Lunch and tea all rolled into one. And what next, I ask you? Where will it all end up? In tears, mark my words.'

Having finally satisfied the demands of her superior, Ida settled herself at the table with her own stacked plate. The good food she'd always enjoyed at Tyson Lodge had fattened her up, and she was no longer the skinny wench she'd been when taken in as a girl by the first Mrs Tyson, picked from the workhouse out of charity. And hadn't that been a red letter day! Ida had never stopped counting her blessings since, even if there'd been far too much work for her to do since Fanny the housemaid had upped and gone to work for Kate, the new Mrs Tyson, making army boots. Fanny was married now and expecting her third, while Ida herself was still here in this kitchen, waiting on everyone hand, foot and finger, in particular Mrs Petty's feet, or saving her legs from walking up and down stairs.

Still, all in all, Ida really felt very content. And she and Mrs Petty did enjoy a good moan together about *them upstairs*. Made life more entertaining, like.

Ida took a huge bite of her fruit loaf and began to talk, spitting a few crumbs as she did so. 'Madam Lucy wanted to know why Mr Tyson hadn't got round to having a second bathroom installed, and sez how a hip bath is *so Victorian! Oi really do h'expect to 'ave hot water at the turn of a tap, Eliot dear.'* Ida attempted to put on a posh voice, mimicking Lucy with wicked accuracy, and Mrs Petty gave a merry chortle, making her several chins shake and producing a loud burp from her over-stuffed stomach.

'Eeh, lass, you'll be the death of me with your intimations. But don't talk with your mouth full, it's rude. If I've told you once… Well, I do hope *you* told *her* that we've better things to do in this house than run up and down stairs with jugs of hot water for the likes of her?'

Ida, who would never dream of saying such a thing to a lady, even one she didn't like, and had simply bobbed a curtsey and scurried away, agreed that she had said exactly that.

'Quite right too. We'll make that madam rue the day she ever set foot in this house again, let alone make the young master out to be a liar. And we have our ways and means, don't we, Ida?'

'Yes, Mrs Petty.'

'Indeed we do. Indeed we do.'

Chapter Eighteen

Eliot's decision drove a wedge between husband and wife. No more frolicking in the bath or tumbling in the hay. Kate lay on her side of the bed in frozen silence, and he on his.

She tried to be understanding, to reason with herself that he had only been trying to be fair. Kate rather thought he'd chosen to believe Lucy rather than Callum because he was already wracked with guilt over his brother Charles's suicide. He'd no wish to make a bad situation even worse. Far easier to sweep the matter under the carpet, in true Tyson fashion, and dismiss past events as an unfortunate childish prank gone wrong.

And on top of all that guilt, Kate was well aware that her husband must still be suffering from the trauma of his war years, so how could she condemn the action he'd taken? He simply wasn't up to making a sound judgement. His soft heart, his great desire for peace and a quiet life, would be bound to affect him, particularly in the light of Callum's continued resentment.

She would have to work on that particular problem, somehow persuade her son to accept the situation, and Eliot as his father. He must learn to put the past behind him.

And she must also work on Eliot. Kate still felt strongly that he'd made a bad mistake and felt duty bound, for the sake of her beloved children, to make him understand this. After a few nights of obstinate silence, and days spent circling each other, avoiding the topic, the situation became unendurable and Kate could bear it no longer. She had to speak.

'You didn't believe him.'

'I've no wish to discuss the matter. The case is closed.'

'It is not a case. This is my son, *our* son, we are talking about here, and you absolutely refuse to believe him.'

'Callum failed to prove his case.'

'But he should be innocent until proven guilty, not the reverse. You made him out to be a liar, and Flora too.'

'They are children, perhaps not properly under-standing the consequences of their sulks and petty actions. You've spoiled them, though who can blame you, in the circumstances?'

''T'was not pettiness, and how can you spoil chil-dren by loving them? I believe what they say. Had you seen Flora that day…'

'That's enough, Kate. I've already told you that the case is closed. I've heard all sides of the argument and made my decision. Like it or not, Lucy is family.

I'm surprised you didn't inform me of this situation years ago, when it all first blew up.'

'I thought you had enough to worry about, with the war, and then your injuries. How could I?'

He looked at her properly then, recognising the sincerity in her soft grey eyes, and remained thoughtful for some moments. 'I can see you might think that. Perhaps you were right, my dear. We will say no more on that score, but now I am home again and the matter has been dealt with, settled once and for all.'

He seemed so cold, so distant. Fear gripped her heart. She couldn't stand to lose him. It didn't bear thinking about. Perhaps she shouldn't push the matter too hard, not at first. It was too soon. She'd need to soften him up slowly, little by little.

Kate wriggled closer to her husband and tentatively stroked his arm. 'And are we still friends? You've been so indifferent towards me these last few days.'

He turned to her then with something of his old eagerness. 'Of course we are still friends. Don't I love you with all my heart? You are my beloved wife and I adore you. Our children will survive and grow out of their sulks and their adolescent moods. Trust me. It's a storm in a teacup. And you and Lucy will learn to get along. Give it a month or two and you'll be like sisters, as Lucy told me you once were.'

'Lucy said we were like *sisters*?'

'She did, both doing your bit for the war effort. So doesn't that prove that I'm right?'

The urge to say that Lucy had barely lifted a finger to justify her existence during the war, demanding to be waited on by Kate as if she were still a servant and not her new sister-in-law, that she was the one who *lied*, was almost overwhelming. Yet Kate hesitated. Where was the point in arguing further? Lucy had won, for now at least.

Besides, any further discussion was halted as Eliot began to kiss her, peeling her nightgown from her shoulders, and Kate was so relieved, so delighted that all was well between them again, that further protests and argument were set aside. There would be time enough later, when Eliot was feeling more himself.

–

Everywhere that Kate went she seemed to hear Lucy's strident voice calling out for Ida, or Mrs Petty, to bring her a tray of tea to the parlour, hot water to her room, a pill for a headache, or to sponge and press a gown. And if they didn't immediately answer her call, she would throw a veritable tantrum and shriek at the top of her voice, demanding to know if there was anyone in the house at all.

'*Is anyone listening to me!*'

Not if I can help it, Kate would think, making a point of hurrying out of sight as quickly as possible. Lucy was frequently in a foul mood because she didn't believe she was receiving the kind of attention she deserved.

'If she *had* got what she deserved, she certainly wouldn't be living like a queen in this house,' Mrs Petty tartly remarked on more than one occasion. Kate always pretended that she hadn't heard.

The French maid had lasted no more than a few days, departing in a huff because she was not allowed to take her meals with the family and thought it beneath her to eat in the kitchen. Not that Kate blamed the poor girl entirely. Mrs Petty was not particularly welcoming, and didn't Kate know how that felt? She had somehow survived her own baptism of fire, which hadn't been easy, involving being sent to Coventry for a number of weeks when she'd first arrived in Mrs Petty's kitchen. But she'd won the cook round in the end.

This poor girl had been less fortunate. There'd been something of a scene the very first day she arrived with Mrs Petty making rather rude remarks about frogs, and Ida doing a good deal of giggling behind her hand over the fancy frocks and furbelows the French maid insisted on wearing. But Ida's laughter had soon turned to sulks when she realised that Madame Celeste, as she liked to be called, expected to be waited on as much as her mistress.

'Nay, I'll not do it. I'll not! 'Oo does she think she is? I told her, ma'am, I did. I'm not paid to wait on the likes of her,' Ida informed Kate, outrage sharp in her voice.

Kate hid a smile. 'I rather think the master would say that you are paid to do whatever he tells you to, and this girl is employed by him and requires feeding.'

'Aye, fair enough,' agreed Mrs Petty, weighing in on Ida's behalf. 'But that doesn't mean she can't fetch her own hot water or clean her own shoes, do it?'

'Er, no,' Kate conceded. 'Perhaps not. But I'd be obliged if you would at least try to get along, for all our sakes. It isn't going to be easy getting used to the changes around here.'

She hadn't needed to spell it out that she meant getting used to having Lucy around, and a chastened Mrs Petty and Ida both promised to do their level best.

Evidently their best wasn't good enough, as the girl left by the end of the first week. The rather superior French maid had made too many demands and, sadly, her fate had been sealed from the start as Mrs Petty did not suffer fools gladly. When Celeste began to criticise her cooking, something previously unheard of, and had insisted that her lamb be cooked rare, not till it was falling off the bone as Mrs Petty liked to do it, she'd been presented with a plateful that was almost raw and stone cold. Celeste had duly taken offence and left.

Lucy was not pleased, and even less so when Eliot refused to replace her, very sensibly pointing out that if Kate could manage without a personal maid, so could she.

It was July before Eliot casually remarked he was ready to return to work. The roses were almost in bloom and Kate had hoped that he would be content to wander in the garden and nurture them into full flower, but it was not to be.

'First thing on Monday morning I intend to go into the office. I am well on the road to recovery, for all my knee still pains me occasionally. It's long past time I got my nose back to the grindstone and take my proper place in charge of Tyson's Shoes, or Tyson Industries as it has now become. You can stay in bed and spoil yourself for a change, my darling.'

'I'd rather come in to the office as usual. I'm in the middle of several matters which require my attention. Customers are depending on me.'

Kate felt some guilt over the way she'd neglected the business in these weeks since Eliot came home. She really should be working on the new designs for the line of ladies' shoes she was planning. Women were now demanding lighter shoes in more fashionable styles, and she and Toby were investigating ways of changing the method of manufacture in order to make this possible.

Toby Lynch had first started working for Kate when she was out on the road, selling her army boots. He was a wiry man in his mid-thirties, of medium height with a tousle of blonde hair and a cheery grin. He'd had plenty of experience in the shoe trade and Kate both liked and trusted him. Since he'd never once let her down, she'd had no hesitation in making him the new foreman of Tyson Industries after Swainson left.

Yet despite Eliot being newly home, she hadn't missed going in to the factory once. Every morning she would slip in for an hour or two, if only to check on progress, to talk things through and reassure herself that all was well. Toby constantly told her to stop worrying and enjoy this precious time with her husband. But Eliot was right. It was time for him to get back to work. It might help him to start looking to the future instead of back into the past.

'I will come in with you. It will give me the chance to explain everything we currently have in hand, since it's your first day.'

'Absolutely not. I forbid it. I can manage perfectly well.'

'But…'

'I will hear no buts.'

Kate adopted her most coaxing tone, using the lilt of her accent and all her feminine wiles to beguile him. 'Will you stop yer blathering and let me do this? Haven't I said that we need to talk, and don't I still need to have a role? I'm not ready to be put out to grass yet awhile. We'd make a good team.'

'Of course we're a team, and your role is clear and straightforward. You are my wife. No, no, my darling, you have done enough. It is my turn to take care of everything now. You can safely leave the factory to me from now on.'

Stubbornly, Kate persisted. 'I shall come in later in the morning, then. I haven't had the chance to properly explain my ideas, my plans for the future. I'll do it then, so I will, when you've had time to get yer bearings.'

Eliot laughed softly, as if humouring her, yet absolutely refused to shift his ground. 'We will discuss them later, over dinner one evening. I will be obeyed in this, Kate, I do not want you at the factory on this day, not on any account.'

And Kate was compelled to let her arguments subside, thinking that perhaps it was fair enough that he be allowed to proceed alone, on his very first day back. Toby would be around to show him the ropes, in any case. And Eliot was still the master after all, perhaps needing to prove that fact, to reassert his authority with the workforce after his long absence. There would be time enough later for discussions and plans.

Eliot left, as promised, shortly after seven but Kate couldn't stay in bed, not for another minute. She was too used to rising early and going into the office. She quickly dressed, took some breakfast, then went about her domestic duties, of which there were few since Mrs Petty ran the establishment with commendable efficiency.

Kate attempted not to think of Lucy triumphantly ensconced in her room upstairs, although she was acutely aware of her presence by the toing and froing of Ida with jugs of hot water and breakfast on a tray. She'd also seen evidence of clothes taken to be pressed and ironed, shoes polished.

Some new house rules would have to be applied. Lucy needed it pointing out to her that the war had affected the servant situation quite badly. Tyson Lodge no longer employed the number of staff it used to in its heyday. Young girls nowadays had far more interesting and remunerative jobs to go to, and a good thing too in Kate's humble opinion. Lucy must learn to fend for herself a little more. She could at least take breakfast downstairs.

Admittedly the installation of one or two more bathrooms might be a good idea. This was the modern age after all, and renovations and refurbishments had been sadly neglected for years because of the war. New bathrooms would save all that carrying of hot water. Kate made a mental note to speak to Eliot on the subject when the moment seemed right.

Callum went off to the factory at his usual time, and Flora to school. Kate saw them both off, tidied up their rooms for want of something to do, and then wondered what to tackle next.

Lucy still hadn't risen, for which Kate was secretly thankful. She really had no wish to see or speak to her.

But Kate was at a loss to know what to do with herself. She was bored, nervous of the long hours, the endless day stretching ahead of her. Never in all her life had she been in a situation where she had time on her hands, hours in which she didn't have the first idea what to do with herself. It felt strangely unsettling.

What on earth did people do when they had no need to work? Kate wasn't really the sort to be content with embroidery or take up charity work as Amelia had done, the first seeming too indolent and frivolous, and the second an affront to human dignity in her opinion.

By eleven o'clock Kate was back in Eliot's study, where she spent the rest of the morning gathering her thoughts and putting the relevant papers in order. It had occurred to her that she would have to move out of here now and so she must make an effort to clear away her things. But where to put them? Where could she work instead?

She began to search for an alternative space, her mind instantly fixing on the small room upstairs on the nursery landing, where she'd spent so much time with Callum when he was a baby. She went straight upstairs to check it out.

Here were the old mahogany drawers, some of them still stuffed with his baby clothes, the little sailor suit and Lord Fauntleroy outfit that Amelia had insisted on buying. Good heavens, these things should have been thrown out years ago.

Kate buried her face in them as she had used to do so often when he was missing, drawing in the scent of her child to ease her aching heart. Now they smelled only of moth-balls, but they held such precious memories how could she possibly discard them?

She wrapped the clothes in tissue paper, along with several other items such as his first baby shoes, Flora's ribbons and christening robe, and put them safely in a box on the top shelf of the old wardrobe.

She found a copy of *Doctor Barker's Advice to Mothers* and began to read it, chuckling softly to herself as memories flooded back. She recalled how she used to pore over these pages, desperately anxious to follow the rules her mistress had set, although more often than not following her own instincts instead.

And here was an ancient bottle of gripe water which reminded her of the Gregory Mixture and Godfrey's Cordial which Amelia had at first expected her to use.

She'd made a start on emptying the top cupboard when the door opened and Lucy herself strolled into the room.

'I thought it must be you in here. What are you doing, cleaning and tidying? Once a servant, always a servant.'

Chapter Nineteen

Kate silently ground her teeth. 'I intend to take over this room as my office.'

'Ah, afraid of having your nose pushed out downstairs?'

'Not at all, but obviously Eliot must have his own study back. I shall move up here.'

Lucy snorted with derision. 'I should think it an ideal choice. Back in the place where you began; where you belong. Eliot is in charge once more, his control over the family restored. Your days of ruling the roost are over. Don't think you'll have any say now in the future running of the business, not now Eliot is back in the saddle.'

'Well, that's where you're wrong. He's more than willing to listen to my ideas. In fact, he's agreed for us to have a short meeting on future business development's this very evening, after dinner.' This was far from the truth but Kate couldn't bear to have Lucy lording it over her.

'Then as a major shareholder, I shall insist that I be present too.'

Kate was startled, mentally kicking herself for mentioning it when she'd hoped for a private meeting. 'The day-to-day running of the business doesn't concern shareholders.'

'Indeed it does.' Lucy took a step into the room and hissed at Kate through tight, narrowed lips, eyes slitted like those of a cat's. 'Don't think you can sideline me, Kate O'Connor, because you can't. I'm back and I intend to stay, so don't try anything you might regret.'

'The name is Tyson. *Mrs* Tyson.'

Lucy put back her lovely head and laughed. 'Call yourself what you will, you're still the girl from Poor House Lane so far as I'm concerned. But as of today, your power is seriously curtailed, your influence over Eliot and Tyson Industries on the wane. Mine is only just starting to rise. Attempt to push me out and I'll make you rue the day. Remember that I've slept with your precious husband once already, and can easily get into his bed again, any time I wish.'

Kate felt as if she'd been punched in the face. Such a possibility had never entered her head. Could it be true? Eliot had never seemed to be the type to wander. He'd been a loyal husband to Amelia, and to herself, Kate was certain of it. But then, there had been that difficult intervening period.

Circumstances, malicious gossip and the loss of Callum, of course, had come between them. Could it have happened then? Surely not. For all Eliot's sense of guilt, he'd had no real time for Lucy. Even so, a doubt had been sown, one Kate would do her best to quash. She certainly had no intention of questioning her husband on the subject because that was clearly what Lucy wanted, to cause dissent between them. 'Sure and you're a terrible liar. I don't believe a word of it.'

'Suit yourself.'

–

Her challenge hadn't quite brought about the effect Lucy had hoped for, but not for one moment would she show her irritation. She'd tried only once to get into Eliot's bed and, much to her chagrin, he had repulsed her. Not that Kate knew that, and Lucy was more than ready to say whatever was necessary to gain control of this household and reinstate her own children in it. Her son Jack should be the one to run the company with Eliot, and take over when he died. It was his birthright.

Her three precious darlings, all away at boarding school, would soon be reaching the end of their school year. She'd made arrangements for them to spend the summer with various school friends, since she couldn't possibly have coped with all three of them at the tiny house in Heversham. It broke her heart, of course, and naturally she missed them, but really children were such hard work.

However, farming them out could now come to an end. There was ample space at Tyson Lodge, and with servants on hand to deal with all the day-to-day unpleasantness involved in caring for the young they would not intrude too much upon her social life.

And they would be delighted by this momentous change in their circumstances.

Young Georgie still had a number of years of education before him, being only fourteen. Darling, irrepressible Bunty should really be sent off to finishing school next year, if only Lucy could persuade Eliot to pay the fees.

But Jack, a year older than his sister at eighteen, was already considering various possibilities for a future career. Not a natural scholar, there was little hope of his going up to Oxford or any other university, and Lucy certainly had no wish for him to enter the services. She held high hopes that, come September, he could be found a position in the business.

What was in Eliot's will, she wondered? It occurred to her then in a sudden flash of intuition that he might not have got around to altering it since Callum returned home. He'd surely made a will before he joined up as most right-thinking men did, or perhaps when he'd married Kate O'Connor, but so far as he was aware at that time, he no longer had a son. Callum was missing, presumed gone for good, in which case the business would naturally go to his next-of-kin, to his nephews and niece. And he surely hadn't had any opportunity, or thought to change it since, being still away at war.

She guessed that until he went to see the family solicitor, should some unforeseen and unfortunate accident happen to Callum, her own children would indeed be the ones to inherit. Who else was there to follow Eliot into the business?

Lucy spared no thought for Kate. So far as Lucy was concerned, she didn't feature in the picture at all. She must now step down from her self-appointed role as head of the family business and be satisfied with simply being a wife and doing as she was told, for a change. Hadn't Lucy herself made a point of emphasising this fact to Eliot? Only, more diplomatically, of course.

As for Flora, she was merely a silly little girl who would no doubt grow up into a silly young woman. Her father might leave her some shares, but never full control. Indeed, the future looked bright, very bright indeed. Although fate may need a helping hand to turn things in the right direction.

Lucy had a sudden urge to be alone, to think through the full implications of this revelatory idea.

As she turned to go, Kate scrambled up from her knees and hurried after her. Grasping the other woman's arm, she jerked her to a halt. 'If it's a battle you're after, you'll not find me frightened of a fight. I never have been. I'm Eliot's wife and the mistress of this house, not you. *I'm* the one who will partner him through life and in business, not you.'

'We'll see about that. We will indeed.'

'And don't you ever try to hurt my children, or you'll be sorry, so help me God.'

Lucy walked away, laughing as if Kate had made some sort of joke.

Mrs Petty enjoyed nothing so much as to prepare dinner for the family. She'd little truck with fancy food and the kind of fashionable dinner parties that the first Mrs Tyson had loved to give, but roast beef and Yorkshire, substantial soups and hearty, rib-sticking puddings were her speciality. There was no one, in all of Westmorland, in her own humble opinion, who could make a better gingerbread, or rum butter. And her Herdwick lamb would melt in the mouth, it was that tender; that French madam had had absolutely no notion of how to judge a good meal.

Today she was preparing individual cottage pies, one for each member of the family, with an extra-large one for the master.

Ida thought this strange, considering it a break with tradition and something of a nuisance since it presented her with more washing up. 'Why are we doing separate pies, Mrs Petty? Wouldn't it be easier to make one big un?'

'Aye, it would, but I have me reasons. Ask no questions and you'll be told no lies.'

Intrigued, Ida's head was suddenly filled with questions she longed to ask as she watched Mrs P mince and cook the beef in a big round pot, adding the onions and tomatoes Ida herself had chopped, together with a few precious herbs; and then prepare a separate, smaller pan, also of minced beef with far fewer vegetables and not even a pinch of pepper.

Frowning, Ida peered into the pan. 'Ooh, this meat's all greasy and full of fat and gristle. What is the butcher thinking of to sell us such rubbish? Shall I chuck it away?'

'No, Ida, you will do no such thing. That's for Madam Lucy's pie.'

Ida's eyes grew round with fright. 'Ooh! That's wicked, that is. She'll notice and blame me.'

Mrs Petty briskly wiped her hands on her apron, the swagger of her plump shoulders loudly proclaiming that she didn't care.

Ida recognised the gesture and quickly added for good measure, 'I'm the one what has to serve her, remember? She'll be furious and make me tek it away. I know she will.'

'She wouldn't dare make a fuss, not yet, not till she feels a bit more secure like. But I'll have a spare one lined up, just in case.'

'Not one of ours?'

'No, Ida, indeed not one of ours. And we shall have some of the very best beef in ours. Folk generally get what they deserve in life, or so I've discovered.'

Dinner, as might be expected, was an uncomfortable affair which passed largely in silence. Lucy took the place she was offered to Eliot's left, and rarely glanced across at Kate, to his right, beyond a venomous glance of triumph as she settled herself at table.

The entire family was present except for Flora, who had been excused as she was still considered to be too young for adult dinner parties. Callum, however, had been bullied into attending, and sat stiffly beside his mother.

The first course, one of Mrs Petty's filling country vegetable soups, was eaten in silence, Ida seeming particularly nervous as she served at table, Kate noticed. Her hands were positively shaking as she put out the individual cottage pies.

'How splendid!' Eliot remarked. 'I get my very own, and much larger than yours, ladies. What is there for afters, Ida? Spotted dick, I hope?'

'Jam roly-poly and custard, sir.'

'Even better,' and everyone smiled at Eliot, humouring his pleasure at the prospect of good, home-cooked food.

Kate had made a private resolve to behave as normally as possible. She turned to Eliot with a brilliant, heart-stopping smile, her blue-grey eyes twinkling with happiness. 'How did your first day go, me darlin'? Not too painful, I hope?'

'It was most – illuminating.'

'Did Toby fill you in on the state of trade and the policies we've been following?'

'He answered a few of my questions, as did many other people I spoke to. I doubt I shall have any trouble in settling back into the routine.'

'Of course you won't.'

'I hope your own day was pleasant, and much less stressful.'

'Er – yes, to be sure.' How could she explain that she'd been bored to tears, that her thoughts for the entire day had been fully occupied with devising a way to get back to work?

Even at the height of his powers, Eliot had never been a natural businessman, much preferring to spend his time tending his garden or painting beautiful pictures, at which he was most skilled. Kate still hoped that he would accept a business partnership between them, with herself remaining actively involved in the day-to-day running of the firm, so that he would have the time to pursue the pleasures he so enjoyed. She meant to talk this through with him, the moment she got the chance.

She cleared her throat. 'Perhaps, after dinner, we could have that meeting concerning future plans for the business? If you remember, Eliot, we discussed it this morning.'

He laid down his knife and fork with a gentle sigh. 'I hope we will be allowed to enjoy our food first, without any further discussion about business matters or your precious plans, my dear?' His smile was kind but his voice firm, and Kate hastened to agree.

'Of course, of course. There will be plenty of time later, at the meeting, for all of that.'

Pleased with Eliot's obvious irritation, Lucy said, 'What a workhorse you are, *sister dear*,' and hid a small smile of satisfaction while quietly pushing aside her own pie, half eaten. If she were in charge of this household, she wouldn't allow such food to be given to the dogs.

The aunts were the only ones to speak after that, remarking politely upon the weather, the charity visits they'd carried out that morning, and the content of the vicar's last sermon. Vera, ever a stickler for propriety and a stalwart of the local church, would obey Eliot to the letter, and dear Cissie, the more mischievous and soft-hearted of the two, would never dream of disagreeing with her sister.

The two maiden ladies, having led a sheltered life, cared for in their youth by their father, then their brother George who had started Tyson's Shoes, and finally by his son, their nephew Eliot, did not believe it their place to question any decision he might make. In their opinion men must be deferred to in all things as they were the ones with the intelligence to make all the essential decisions in life, the ones who ruled the world, as certainly Eliot ruled their own small portion of it.

Even so, Vera rather hoped that they too would be invited into the meeting, yet not for a moment would she say as much.

Once the pudding dishes had been cleared away and coffee served, Kate tried again. 'Shall we repair to the study now, to have our meeting?'

Her heart sank just a fraction as Eliot glanced across at her with a startled expression in his eyes, almost as if he'd forgotten the subject had ever been mentioned.

Aware of Lucy's smirk of satisfaction, Kate ploughed on, smiling all the while to soften the force of her words, trying to still the disquiet that was eating into her soul over her husband's emotional state. Hadn't he only just returned from the war? Wasn't he bound to be a bit confused from time to time? He was settling, was he not, and would improve still further with time, love and patience. The trouble was that decisions about the business couldn't afford to wait. Something had to be done to protect its future now.

'Now that you feel well enough to face work again, I think it important you be put fully in the picture. I would welcome the opportunity to put forward the ideas I have in mind to help make the business more sound.'

His mouth twisted slightly at the corners, as if her earnestness amused him. 'If you insist, though it seemed sound enough to me. However, I can see I shall get no peace until you do.'

'I don't *insist*, Eliot, I simply think it might be useful.' Oh, and it would be so lovely, she wanted to add, to have a few private moments alone with her husband while she did so: to escape Lucy's eagle eye and the aunts' condescending disapproval.

She was to be disappointed in this. Even as she rose, cup and saucer in hand, Lucy did likewise.

'As shareholders, I believe the three of us should also be present at any board meeting. We too need to be kept fully in the picture. Don't you agree, Eliot?'

Vera was scrambling to her feet, delighted this suggestion had been made without her having to make it. 'Indeed, what a splendid idea. I should be most interested to hear your plans too, Kate dear.'

'And I,' Cissie put in, in case anyone should forget that she was there.

Eliot sighed with resignation. 'I can see I am being bullied from all sides, whether I like it or not. Very well, Lucy, Aunts, if you think you won't be too bored.'

'Of course I shan't be bored,' said Lucy. 'Not in the slightest.'

Chapter Twenty

The meeting was not a success. Kate explained all about her dreams for developing a ladies' fashion line using a new process by which the outer soles were cemented instead of being stitched or welted on. Eliot was not impressed, claiming she was suggesting that Tyson's produce lightweight rubbish.

'The shoes will be lightweight, yes, but certainly not rubbish. Not in the least. Tyson's will continue to be known for its quality footwear. But the latest fashions demand that women show off their ankles, and they want pretty, delicate shoes to give the appearance of pretty, delicate feet. It is simple vanity, yes, but we must pander to fashion if we are to make progress in the post-war era. Toby has come up with a way of inserting a soft rubber pad under the insole, which supports the instep. We must also provide shoes in different widths and different fittings. Not all women have the same shape of foot, even if they are the same size. We should accommodate that fact. And we must advertise.'

'*Advertise*? Tyson's have never needed to stoop so low in the past. Why should we start now?' Eliot asked, in a tone which set advertising on a par with opening a brothel.

'Advertising is going to become increasingly important as firms compete for business through what could be a nasty post-war slump.'

'*The Times* is saying quite the opposite, predicting the boom will last.'

'Excellent. I hope they are right. However, we must make sure that we are a part of it if it does, and can survive if it doesn't.'

Eliot made a sound something like 'Harrumph!' He was beginning to feel like an outsider, a stranger in his own company, in his own home almost. Nothing was quite the same in his home-town of Kendal, or England for that matter. Women were working and yet skilled men were in short supply since so many had been killed. Prices were soaring. Station porters were earning three pounds a week, while officers and gentlemen were walking the streets with no job to go to at all.

Lloyd George's government seemed hell-bent on bringing in all manner of legislation to control the railways, roads, canals and docks, working hours and wages, even intending to meddle in land with an iniquitous new tax. They'd be nationalising all of industry before long, the way they were going on.

Even his own wife was lecturing him.

Eliot almost longed for the regular routine of parade and drill, of giving his men their orders which they obediently carried out. Simple. Much easier than all of this politics, the constant discussion of boom or bust, this confusion of choices and worrying need for decisions.

He wanted things to continue exactly as they had before the war, when Swainson ran things for him without bothering him about trifles. Instead of which he had this Toby Lynch character knocking on his door every five minutes wanting a decision on this, that, or the other. Eliot longed for a placid backwater, for peace!

Kate was saying, 'We must create eye-catching posters and let everyone know what wonderful shoes Tyson's produces. That we offer style and fashion, show how much trouble we take to provide the correct fitting. Ladies must be able to buy our shoes with confidence.'

Lucy said, 'My word, you seem to have thought this out most thoroughly. All carefully planned even before dear Eliot has had the chance to settle in.'

Eliot frowned, clearly not liking the inference behind her remark.

Kate simply ignored her. 'It will be good for Kendal, and good for the men newly returned from the trenches to know that they have a long and secure future with the firm. Don't you see, Eliot, that this is the way forward? The war is over, now we must make shoes for a new peace.'

But he didn't see. Or at least, if he did, he wasn't admitting as much.

Lucy's remark had hit home and Kate could tell that he hated the fact that she had come up with the idea first, before him. He was even jealous of Toby Lynch for having solved some of the manufacturing problems in order to produce this lighter footwear.

'I will think about your suggestions,' he said, rather portentously. 'And make my decision when I am good and ready. I thank you for minding the factory for me, Kate. You've done a splendid job, but I am the master, don't forget, and I won't allow Tyson's to become the kind of factory which produces slipshod work.'

'Hear, hear,' echoed Lucy, who wouldn't have known a well-made shoe from a bad, caring only for the look of the thing.

Kate sighed, trying to smile and appear unconcerned. My goodness, but he'd grown proud and obstinate. It was one thing to refuse to use a walking stick when he was clearly in pain, quite another to risk the livelihood of the entire workforce. However, she wasn't yet ready to admit defeat, although persuading her husband to agree to her plan wasn't going to be nearly as straightforward as she'd hoped.

After the meeting, Lucy waylaid Eliot and took the opportunity to put in a word for Jack. 'He has completed his education and will soon be seeking a situation. I trust there will be… I mean, I rather hoped that he might…' Lucy was appalled by her own dithering. What on earth was the matter with her? Could it have something to do with the bland expression of disinterest on Eliot's face, which gave the impression that he wasn't even properly listening to her? She straightened her spine. 'What I am trying to say, Eliot, is that I assume there will be a place for him at Tyson's? He is family, after all. Your own brother's eldest son.'

'I am aware of who he is.'

'And then there is darling Bunty, who really must be properly finished.'

'Must she indeed?' He raised one dark eyebrow in that way he had when something amused him.

He might give every impression of taking life seriously, which he deemed appropriate where his own offspring were concerned, but when it came to his nephews and niece, it was quite a different matter. They were apparently to be viewed as some sort of joke. Lucy made up her mind to say so, but then Kate chose that moment to walk through the hall and he half turned away to follow her.

'Eliot?' Lucy grabbed him by the arm to remind him that he still hadn't answered her question. 'I was asking about Jack. He *is* to join the management team in September, isn't he? I would like to reassure him that his future is settled.'

'Lucy dear, I confess I haven't given a single thought to your son's future. That is for you, and for him, to decide. Nothing to do with me. Now, if you will excuse me? I believe this meeting is closed.'

And he walked away, following that trollop up the stairs while Lucy was left fuming in the hall, and in full view of that dreadful servant girl, Ida.

'Don't you have a bed to go to?' Lucy snapped.

'I were just locking up. Would there be anything more you'd be wanting, ma'am?' It was past eleven and Ida was dropping on her feet; would be most thankful to get to her bed, if ever she got the chance.

'Bring a cup of hot milk to my room. Quickly, girl! I haven't all night.' Then she stuck her chin in the air and marched upstairs.

Ida returned to the kitchen, heated some milk, spat very gently into it, stirred it well, and took it upstairs to Lucy with all haste, as she had been bidden.

—

From that day on, Eliot didn't miss a day at the factory. He would rise at seven, enjoy an excellent breakfast, and sharp at eight would arrive in his office, having walked along the river path for the short distance between the two places. Kate would sit with him while he ate, watch him leave, but never once did he ask her to accompany him. On the contrary, he still obstinately refused to allow her to come into the factory at all.

'You have done your duty,' he would say, whenever she suggested it, or risked asking if he'd made up his mind yet about her proposed new line of ladies' shoes. 'And now I must do mine. I will keep you informed as to what I decide.'

'I should hope so, Eliot, since I own a part of the business too,' she gently reminded him on one occasion. 'I believe I should have a say over what happens to my own section of the company, at least. Now that my workers can no longer make army boots, we must find other orders, other ways forward.'

It was the wrong thing to say.

'They are no longer *your* workers, Kate, and Tyson's Shoes is safe in my hands, as indeed it always has been. You own a mere ten per cent, and since you are my wife and our lives and individual businesses completely merged, you can trust me to make the right decisions, as I did in the past.'

Kate was equally obstinate. 'I don't think so, Eliot. It isn't about trust, do you see, and things are no longer as they used to be in the past. We should be equal partners. The war, and the development of my own business, changed everything. I must insist upon being involved in any decision about the direction the company might take in the future.'

He was clearly irritated by her persistence. 'There are a great many women making demands they have no right to make. I didn't see any of them at the front when the going got tough.'

'Really? I believe there were some nurses pretty near to it,' Kate patiently remarked. 'Many of us were not at the front, I'll admit, although we kept you men well supplied with boots and armaments so that you could do your job properly, which means we have indeed earned the right for our voices to be heard. Now stop being so stubborn, Eliot, and agree that the world has changed.'

But he would not.

Kate was forced to resort to subterfuge, as women throughout time had found it necessary to do in order to achieve their goal. Two or three times a week she would wait until he was gone, then later in the morning she would sneak into the factory when she knew Eliot would be occupied. She was careful not to be seen by anyone, but it was not easy.

She would have a quiet meeting with Toby behind closed doors, perhaps going on afterwards to visit the odd customer. She would love to have examined progress in the new design department that she'd set up but daren't take the risk. They'd be bound to mention to Eliot that she'd been in.

And Kate really had no wish to offend or embarrass him by an open confrontation despite being desperate to remain involved. She kept hoping that she would eventually win him round by quiet persuasion, but he remained adamant that her role was now that of his wife and helpmate, and nothing more, a situation she found hard to accept.

She even shocked herself by resenting the fact that Eliot had reclaimed use of his own study, for all she'd anticipated his doing so. There was her little hideaway upstairs, of course, the old nursery which she'd fitted out as a small office. But whenever she went up there to work, she was aware of Lucy's laughter and constant derision.

'Yes, go back to the nursery where you belong. Shall we have your meals sent up, as we used to? What would you like? Toast soldiers and jam? Rice pudding?'

It was hateful, and when she'd closed the door on Lucy's taunts, Kate found that she had little to occupy her, even there. She felt she was losing touch, being shut out of her own business.

Toby did his best to keep her informed on the days she didn't go in, sending her little notes, telling her of meetings held and decisions made without her presence or knowledge, offering to call round and explain things properly to her.

Kate always refused to allow him to come to the house. The last thing she needed was to be caught holding clandestine discussions in the summer house with the foreman, thereby providing ammunition for Lucy to inform on her to Eliot, or maliciously accuse her of being involved in some sort of affair.

She tried a different tactic. 'Could I come and work in the design room, mebbe? I'm so bored at home, Eliot, with not enough to do. Could I not at least have the opportunity to express my ideas in some other way? I swear I'll not interfere in the decision-making process, or the actual running of the factory.'

'I will consider it, my dear, but knowing you as I do, I suspect this is merely a new means of trying to get your own way.' He kissed her as he said this, which quite took the sting out of his words, although of course he was absolutely correct.

'How could you ever keep your delightful nose out of what I was doing? You would expect every one of your designs to be chosen, the work implemented forthwith, decisions made of which you approve. I cannot allow that, Kate.

'Apart from the fact that you are my wife and I wish to take care of you, keep you safe at home, we do not see eye to eye on the future of the company. Tyson's Shoes has an image to maintain, a quality and standard which is not in keeping with your feminine nonsense of pretty-pretty lightweight rubbish. So do stop fretting and relax. If you have too much time on your hands, take up gardening. I always found it very therapeutic.'

It was so utterly infuriating and frustrating. And then something happened which changed everything.

Chapter Twenty-One

They were sitting in the summer house on a lovely August evening, the sun setting over Castle Hill, lining grey clouds with pink and gold in a cobalt blue sky, the river a slick of silver in the fading light. Kate had finally made the decision to give him her news. She'd kept the information to herself for several weeks, needing time to grow accustomed to the idea.

Of course she was thrilled, but at the same time stunned, knowing it would mean she must finally put her ambitions on hold.

Toby had told her recently that new orders were thin on the ground, that if something didn't happen soon he would be forced to lay men off. Eliot resisted all offers of help and it worried and frightened her. What would happen if there was a slump and the company went under? Kate had experienced poverty, had tasted its bitterness. She'd certainly no wish to return to Poor House Lane again.

She'd tried to advise from the wings, as it were, making suggestions and comments which generally were not welcomed. Eliot seemed to view her interest as a threat, yet Kate felt sure Tyson's was losing its way, not replacing the orders for army boots with anything new.

Her darling husband had never been the most diligent or gifted of businessmen, somehow lacking vision and flair, although he'd always done his best and generally managed to rise to a challenge. But he couldn't even seem to do that nowadays.

Despite a long and difficult summer in which he'd eased himself gently back into work, he still became easily confused, and his periods of depression were lifting only slightly.

Perhaps her present condition might make him realise that she wasn't attempting to usurp his role after all, that she had another which gave her equal fulfilment.

Even so, Kate had no intention of giving up her interest in the business entirely. Her private meetings with Toby remained a regular part of her life, and could surely continue, for she was in no way incapacitated. She still lived in hope of finding some non-confrontational way of persuading her husband round to her way of thinking. Her patience and skill had been exemplary, if she said so herself.

The thought brought a smile to her face. Maybe pride in new fatherhood would do the trick.

'You know that although I would love to be back at the factory, fully involved as I used to be, because I love to work…'

Eliot interrupted her with a heavy sigh. 'We've been through all of this Kate, *ad nauseam*. I believe the subject is closed.'

'I know, I know, and *you* know that it doesn't make the slightest difference to our life together, not one bit. I'm more than happy simply to be your wife and the mother of your children, and haven't I accepted that these last months?' This wasn't strictly true, as they were both well aware, but Kate was doing her utmost to appear content with her new status.

Eliot said, 'I'm glad to hear it. Other women have been happy to step down, now that their husbands are returned to them.' The grooves etched beside the corners of his mouth, Kate noticed, seemed deeper than ever, with no hint of a smile as he looked at her, ready to fend off further argument. His leg still pained him badly, and he obstinately refused to use his stick.

'It was just that I felt I had so much to offer, and so little to do here that Mrs Petty can't do a thousand times better.' Wanting to bring a smile to lift the corners of that dejected mouth, Kate continued, 'But then, when did I ever have the chance to learn to be a housekeeper in Poor House Lane? We couldn't keep ourselves clean there, let alone the stinking hole in which we lived. Didn't Amelia despair of me ever learning civilised ways, even in the nursery?'

'I'd rather you didn't speak of Poor House Lane,' Eliot said, rather stuffily.

'Why not, 'tis the simple truth? That's where I lived, and bore Callum.'

'And now you are free of it, so we need never refer to it again, if you don't mind.'

'Oh, don't be such an old stuffed shirt! Is it ashamed of me you are? And here's me trying to tell you something exciting. I'm saying I dearly *would* love to be involved in finding and creating designs for new lines, but I can't after all. If I started work, sure I'd have to leave in no time.'

He looked at her, startled, his face frozen with shock. 'Leave? You're leaving me?'

'Jesus, Mary and Joseph, I never meant that I'm leaving you, you daft eejit! Why would I do that? Not while I've breath in me body. That's not what I meant at all. Only I'm going to have other things to occupy me over the next few months, something far more important to do with my time. The next year or so, I'd say.'

'And what that might be?'

'Can't ye guess?'

He looked into her dancing eyes and felt his whole body grow still. 'You're not!'

Kate dissolved into a fit of giggles. 'To be sure I am.'

'Oh, my darling, I don't believe it. You're…' Eliot was so delighted, so beside himself with happiness, he dare hardly say the words.

Understanding perfectly, Kate said it for him. 'Aye, you can say it, 'cos it's true. I'm expecting. All them shenanigans we've been up to lately has had the expected result. It seems I'm not quite over the hill at thirty-two. Young enough anyways to make you a da again. Now will you give me a kiss, you old grumpy, and then smile a bit more, just to please me.'

-

Lucy was completely absorbed in watching Callum. She noted what time he rose in the mornings, how long he took over breakfast, even what he ate, generally bread and dripping, proving he was a common farmhand still.

She would covertly watch as he pulled on his jacket, picked up his knapsack with his lunch box inside and headed off to the factory every morning sharp at seven, just as he was doing now.

Not that she rose this early every morning, but it was worth getting up on the odd occasion in order to observe what he did, what his habits were. One never knew when information, knowledge of any kind, might come in handy.

She'd certainly once made good use of the fact that his stupid sister found eggs abhorrent. Those kind of tactics would not serve for a grown boy, nearly a young man, naturally. Nor could she simply spirit him away to the workhouse this time. She would need to be much more subtle, far cleverer.

But then she was clever. And this time she must make it permanent. Lucy could not risk being discovered again trying to harm him, or her pleas of innocence would sound very thin, very thin indeed.

She might well have got away with her crime the first time around, had Callum not returned to Kendal market, his curiosity stirred by meeting Flora, that hint of red in her dark brown hair betraying her Irish ancestry, and her pale, freckled face so like the remembered image of his mother's.

The unreliable memories of a young boy had brought Lucy shame and exile, near poverty and humiliation, living upon the charity of friends. Finally, when even they had grown tired of her, she'd been compelled to endure a miserable existence in the aunts' fusty old-fashioned house in Heversham. It stank of dogs and mothballs, with not a flicker of sunlight filtering through the leaded windows because of all the overgrown trees and shrubs in the tiny garden. Lucy had deliberately put up with the inconvenience, choosing to guard her privacy from prying eyes rather than bask in light and sunshine.

Oh, but she'd resented her exile. She most certainly had. She had a lot of ground to make up.

Later in the day, she would take out her brand new Austin 20, so distinctive and high-class, and drive it around town for a little while, calling on one or two of the few friends she still had left, for afternoon tea and a gossip.

When she'd grown weary of hearing Adeline Cross list the great accomplishments of her children, or Felicity Goodchild proclaiming how splendidly her husband was doing, Lucy would climb back into her motor and drive herself home again. Except that she would make a slight detour. She always judged the time precisely, so that she reached the factory at the exact moment Callum would be leaving.

Not that she ever offered him a lift. She would park up a side street and watch as he walked or cycled up Aynam Road with his chums. Five-thirty, without fail, every day.

Evenings seemed to be fully occupied, with Callum rarely spending one at home. On Mondays and Thursdays he attended a class at the Allen Technical College, something to do with bookkeeping. On Tuesdays he went up to Kendal Green for a game of football with his mates, and sometimes he would go to the swimming baths in Allhallows Lane.

On Fridays he always called at the library to change his book before going out for a beer to one of the less salubrious establishments in town, certainly in Lucy's opinion, who preferred the County or possibly the White Lion which were most commodious and comfortable.

She'd followed him only once or twice, simply to ascertain that he drank at what were known locally as Jerry shops, typical of his low-brow tastes. His favourite was either the Rifle Man's Arms or the Odd Fellows' Arms. He didn't seem to be a heavy drinker, which was unfortunate, and generally left well before closing time, being home by nine-thirty. Young Callum was becoming a most sober, right-minded citizen, and quite the scholar, or so he imagined, which made her task more difficult.

What she would do with all this information, Lucy hadn't quite made up her mind. But by God, she meant to do something.

—

'You called me a stuffed shirt.'

Kate giggled, snuggling close against her husband beneath the sheets, twining her legs about his. They wasted no time in going early to bed that night, longing to be alone and revel in their joyous news. Eliot had been nervous at first, fearful of hurting her, but Kate had reassured him and they'd made love with such tenderness that afterwards she'd wept in his arms. 'And so ye are a stuffed shirt, so self-righteous and pompous these days. The fault of the army, not you. Don't you need to learn how to relax and stop worrying so much? The war is over and the world is not going to blow up in yer face, nor crash and bang in your head any more. You're free, m'darlin'. Free as a bird.'

'To love you, and give you more children.'

'And isn't that the truth of it.'

'I don't want you to have to work.'

'Sure and of course I don't *have* to work. I just want to, and where's the wrong in that, will ye tell me? You were happy enough for me to run the company single-handed throughout the war, so what's changed? I'm still the same person, still as capable, still as argumentative and infuriating.'

He laughed. 'You can say that again.'

She smiled softly at him, loving him so much it hurt. This small miracle seemed to have brought them close again, and Kate couldn't have been happier. 'Will you at least give me a chance? Maybe I could do a bit of work at home, if you'd let me? And then when the babby is born and I'm on me feet again, we could get a nursemaid so I could come in to the factory. Not every day mind, just two or three mornings a week, mebbe. How would that be?'

'I'll think about it.'

'You promise me?'

'I've said I will think about, haven't I? A man's word is his bond.' Eliot's voice was grave but his eyes were laughing at her, twinkling merrily.

'Well then, because I'm only a simple woman, I shall need you to seal your promise with a kiss.'

'I have no problem with that.' And he pulled her close to smooth his hand over her breasts, the ripening curve of her belly, and kiss her deeply and passionately.

'Will we tell them soon, tomorrow mebbe?'

'Must we?'

'Callum and Flora will need time to get used to the idea that their mammy is still capable of making love, let alone having more children. And the aunts'll

267

want to start knitting. You know how they are. Getting ready for the babby will keep them happily occupied for hours on end. And sure as hell is hot, I certainly can't knit.'

'Kate!'

'Well, isn't that the truth? Remember when Amelia tried to teach me? More holes than knitting there was.' And they both laughed fondly at the memory then fell silent as they recalled how that was during her last illness, a sad and poignant time.

'Do you miss her still?' Kate tentatively asked and Eliot looked at her for a long moment, unspeaking, then gathered her lovely elfin face between his two hands.

'I loved Amelia, as you well know, but I love you too. I love you more than life itself, if that doesn't sound too trite. I'm a very lucky man to have had so much love in my life.'

–

Kate's piece of news came like a bolt from the blue to Lucy. 'You're expecting *again*? Good God!'

'I was rather stunned too, but so pleased.'

Eliot put an arm about his wife and hugged her to his side. 'We both are. Isn't it wonderful news, Lucy?'

'Absolutely marvellous,' she agreed, struggling to disguise the sour edge to her tone. It felt as if shards of ice were stabbing her insides. Another child! It was unendurable. Where was the point now in incapacitating Callum when another boy could well replace him in a matter of months? The woman bred like a rabbit. Who knew how many more brats she might have before she was done?

Lucy was silently fuming. She'd been considering calling upon Swainson, the foreman who had once worked for the firm and been dismissed for taking advantage of the women. She'd thought he might assist her by breaking the boy's legs. She'd been so looking forward to seeing this workhouse brat confined to a wheelchair, which would not only have put an end to any hope of his running the factory, but also to his swimming and his football, as well as his nights out at the beer shops. It would have made his life an utter misery which was exactly what he deserved. Serve him right for not having stayed where she'd put him.

But something, she wasn't sure what, had held her back. Now she knew that wouldn't achieve her ends at all, not with another child on the way.

Then what was the answer? Should some desperately unfortunate accident happen to Kate herself, thereby disposing of the expected infant? But that would still leave Callum as heir, and Eliot in charge.

Flora, of course, was of no consequence, and could easily be controlled. So far, Lucy had exercised that power merely by a look, delighting in making the child shiver with fear. But she was willing to go further, if she felt it necessary. She was willing to go to any lengths.

But first she needed to think through all the implications of this new development, to plan carefully. Nothing must be rushed.

Lucy continued with her normal routine, her mind a turmoil of emotion as she strove to find a solution to her dilemma. Young Georgie had plenty of time on his side, but Jack and Bunty would be home by September, and she was determined to have something worthwhile to offer them by then. She continued with her afternoon vigils and a day or two later was parked in her usual spot, hidden up a side street some distance from the factory but with a good view of Aynam Road, along which Callum must walk. He was late today and she was growing tired of waiting. Lucy had almost decided to give up, in view of the changed circumstances. Where was the point? She must devise some other plan. The anger and resentment she felt towards the whole lot of them festered deep inside of her.

Kate O'Connor had no right to so much happiness, to lord it over her as the mistress of Tyson Lodge, let alone be constantly nagging Eliot to allow her to help run the factory as well. The woman had grown above herself and needed bringing down a peg or two, back to where she belonged, in the gutter.

Neither did Eliot have any right to disinherit his own brother's children for the sake of a workhouse brat. It was intolerable. Lucy would never forgive him for that, not for as long as she lived. If he'd left the boy to rot in Poor House Lane, her darling husband Charles might still have been alive today, she thought, conveniently forgetting that Charles's suicide had been caused by debt which she herself had helped him to accumulate.

And then she saw Eliot come out of the factory and start to walk up Aynam Road, more of a hobble in fact, favouring his injured leg as he always did. When he reached the corner of Nether Bridge, he would cross the road and call in the corner shop for his evening paper.

And suddenly the answer came to her. Neat and simple.

The engine was ticking over nicely, and it took no time at all to slip it into gear, hit the accelerator and surge forward, the power of the engine exciting her. There was even time to catch the startled expression in Eliot's eyes as he focussed upon her at the moment of impact, and then his body was flying upwards, right over the top of the car.

Chapter Twenty-Two

Lucy didn't wait to find out where or how his body landed, she pressed her foot to the floor on the accelerator, skidded left over Nether Bridge, left again, and was soon racing away from town, quite certain that no one would have had the chance to take the number of her car. There'd been some old dear standing on her doorstep but Lucy was quite certain she wouldn't have been near enough to identify the driver.

She found that she was gasping for breath, her nerves a jangle of excitement and terror. Oh, but she had never enjoyed herself more in all of her life. Seeing a policeman come into view ahead, she slowed the car down to the correct fifteen miles an hour. She mustn't get too carried away. It was vital that she remain free from all suspicion.

Lucy made a wide detour of the town as quickly as she possibly could without drawing attention to herself, and miraculously was back home with the Austin parked in the garage within ten minutes. She slipped quietly in through a side door, calling for Ida to bring her a tray of tea to the parlour at once, as if she'd been there all along. Most satisfactory.

The doorbell rang. No sound permeated up the wide stairs to indicate that Ida was rushing to answer it, and Kate correctly surmised that she was engaged in some task for Lucy. She seemed to be constantly answering to her beck and call these days. Mrs Petty could well be out in the garden, collecting vegetables for dinner, or else gossiping with young Tom in the afternoon sunshine. Kate glanced at the clock. It was early yet, not quite five. With a sigh, she set down the pile of books she'd been sorting, wiped the dust from her hands on her apron, and hurried downstairs.

It was the local constable who was patiently waiting for her, and even before he spoke, the look on his face told her everything. She felt, in that moment, as if time stood still, yet the chimes of the grandfather clock in the hall sounded louder than ever, and a chill descended upon her, despite the August heat.

'I'm that sorry, Mrs Tyson. Happen it would be best if you sat down.'

'Oh, dear God… Callum?'

'No, ma'am, don't fret none about your boy. It's – well, fact of the matter is…' This was the one part of his job that the constable hated the most. 'Is there anyone else in the house, ma'am? Can I call someone for you?'

'Please, get on with it. What's happened?'

'Well, the car didn't even stop, d'you see. It was all very quick. The master wouldn't even have known what had hit him. He were just walking across Aynam Road, limping like, one witness said. War injury, I dare say. He should have used a stick. Too proud, no doubt. Anyway, the motor car swung round the corner and ploughed straight into him. Like I say, didn't even stop, the villain went shooting off out of town at the speed of light. We're trying to find out the make and registration number but all we know for sure is that it was black, which doesn't help us much at all, does it? I mean, what else would it have been? All cars are black. The poor man didn't stand a chance. Blinded by the lowness of the sun to see proper, I expect. I can't tell you how sorry I am, ma'am. Never was a nicer bloke, and him just back from the front. Missed all them German bullets and bombs, only to cop it in his own town.'

The constable seemed to be asking and answering his own questions. Which was just as well since Kate was quite incapable of doing so. She'd passed out on Ida's clean doorstep.

–

The funeral took place early the following week at Kendal Parish Church where the vicar gave a lengthy eulogy on what a very fine gentleman Mr Eliot Tyson had been; how well thought of he was in the town, by townsfolk and factory workers alike; how brave he'd been in volunteering for active service;

and how tragic it was that having survived the war, he had not managed to survive the peace.

The respect and high esteem in which he'd been held were only too evident in a church that was packed to the door. Hymns were sung, prayers chanted and psalms read, before he was laid to rest in the parish churchyard.

Not that Kate was aware of any of this. She had been rushed to the County hospital where she'd lost her baby and had since lain in a stupor, unaware of anything going on around her.

All of which suited Lucy perfectly.

The reading of the will, some three weeks after Eliot's death, delayed out of respect for Kate's condition, was the first day she felt able to rise from her bed and come downstairs. She would not have achieved even this had it not been for dear Aunt Cissie's help and quiet insistence.

'I shall help to get you washed and dressed, dear girl, but it is essential that you are present. You must hear what is being said.'

And when Kate turned away with a groan, complaining that she didn't care what the will said, she simply wanted to be left alone, Cissie became surprisingly firm.

'You must get up, you really must. Lucy will be there, with all her children. They have arrived in force, don't you know? Jack, Bunty and even young George, dragooned into action to prove they are "family"; that they care. How would poor Callum and Flora feel if you weren't present too, right beside them? Or are you going to throw in the towel and allow Lucy to take over?'

If anything was calculated to galvanise her into action, it was the thought of Lucy taking charge.

Kate submitted herself to Cissie's ministrations. A bath was drawn, her face and hands washed like a child's, her back scrubbed and her hair shampooed, the fresh lemon verbena scent of it making her cry as she recalled how much Eliot had loved it. Then she was tenderly dried and dressed in the frock she generally wore for other people's funerals, had never intended to wear for anyone so close to her as her own husband. It all seemed unreal, as if she were one step removed from everything, standing behind a pane of frosted glass, not quite able to see or hear what was going on beyond it.

With her face wax-pale and her hair neatly tied back Kate walked slowly downstairs, supported by Cissie every step of the way, to take her place in Eliot's study. Every day throughout the war she had occupied that room without a second thought, now she hesitated at the door, summoning every ounce of her strength before she was able to face the prospect of entering.

'Be brave, dear girl, you are not alone. Vera and I will be right there beside you, as always,' Cissie said, patting her hand.

Kate felt a rush of warm gratitude. 'Thank you.' She wanted to say so much more, about how she appreciated the support the aunts had given her so often in the past, despite their initial disapproval of her, but knew that she couldn't, not without starting the tears all over again.

Vera opened the door and the two maiden ladies helped Kate to a seat right in the centre of the circle of chairs set before Eliot's desk. The leather seat was cracked and she could feel the horse-hair stuffing pricking the back of her legs, but didn't ask for a better one or shift her position. The discomfort would serve to keep her mind on what was going on.

It seemed wrong to Kate that a stranger, Mr Jeffries the family solicitor, should be seated at Eliot's desk. She wanted to shout at him to go away, to tell him that her husband would not approve of his presence here. The aroma of Eliot's after-dinner cigar still lingered in the air, an acrid, stale odour that brought a rush of fresh tears to Kate's eyes. Would she ever get through this ordeal?

Kate was aware of Lucy and her three children, of Mrs Petty and Ida and the two aunts, all watching her with varying degrees of sympathy and concern. She must look what she was, a vulnerable young woman grieving for a beloved husband; a woman who'd just lost a precious child and had suddenly aged by ten years.

She also noticed that Callum was not present.

A small warm hand slid into hers. 'Are you all right, Mammy? Aunt Cissie said you were ill and that I was not to disturb you.'

'Flora, me darlin', how good it is to see you. Sure and Mammy's on the mend now. Can't you see?'

'Shall we proceed?' This from Lucy who, as Cissie quite rightly stated, had clearly put herself in charge. But then she'd no doubt organised the entire funeral since Kate had been incapable.

The solicitor cleared his throat, declared that this was Eliot Tyson's last will and testimony, and began to read.

Most of it went right over Kate's head. She was quite incapable of concentrating. She felt so restless and desperately tired. Even sitting in a chair took every ounce of her willpower. All she wanted to do was to crawl back upstairs, put her head under the bedclothes, go to sleep and never wake up. Except that was a wicked thought. What would happen to her children then? She mustn't even think such a thing.

Mr Jeffries seemed to be explaining how a small portion of the business already belonged entirely to Kate, and that Eliot's will concerned only the ninety per cent of Tyson's that he owned. She lost track of his comments after that, as it all became far too convoluted and complicated.

She did hear that there were small legacies for Mrs Petty and even Ida which pleased her as it would secure their future at least. She heard the names of

Lucy's children mentioned, though in what connection she couldn't have said. The outcome must have pleased Lucy for she gave a satisfied little grunt at one point, visibly relaxing as she cocked a look of pure triumph in Kate's direction.

When it was done and the document folded away, Lucy rose gracefully and personally thanked the solicitor, shaking his hand before sweeping out of the room, nose in the air, her children following close behind, without a second glance at Kate.

The main body of the complicated document had to be explained to Kate all over again afterwards, over a nice cup of tea which Mrs Petty brought to the small parlour.

The will had apparently been written at the time of their marriage, shortly after Eliot had joined up, he'd therefore made no direct provision for Callum, since the boy had still been missing at the time. The only mention of him was in the instruction: *In the event of my adopted son Callum being found I trust my wife Katherine to make due provision for him out of her share of my estate as my sister-in-law Lucy must do likewise with her own children.*

Apparently this had met with Lucy's approval.

Mr Jeffries went on to explain how the house and Eliot's personal effects and disposable funds were left to her in entirety. Now he paused, making sure that he had her full attention before continuing.

Following one or two charitable bequests and a codicil added later to set up a trust fund for Flora, the business known as Tyson Shoe Industries, *shall be divided equally between my wife Katherine and my sister-in-law Lucy Tyson widow of my brother Charles. I trust that as the sisters they have now become they will feel able to work together to maintain the high standards of Tyson Shoe Industries. I leave my company safely in their hands.*

Chapter Twenty-Three

Callum felt as if he was burning up inside with hatred and resentment. This wasn't how it was meant to be. Finding his mother had been the answer to his prayers, and even though things hadn't always gone smoothly between them, at least they were getting to know each other. And he'd been so grateful to get away from the Brocklebanks and that dreadful farm.

It crossed his mind that Mrs Brocklebank must have wondered what had happened to him, where he'd run off to on that market day. Not that he really cared what she thought. He was free. He had found his mother again. That was all that mattered.

Kate was kind and loving, and he liked her helping him with his reading. He'd been enjoying those lessons, that peaceful time together, at least until Eliot Tyson had poked his nose in. He hadn't been near the study since, of course. He'd not be held up as a laughing stock, not by anyone.

Accepting Eliot Tyson as his father had been one step too far, too much to ask. Callum was ashamed to say that he felt no great sorrow over his death, except for the grief it was causing Kate. Not only had she lost her husband, but the child she was carrying too.

Callum felt sorry for her. She rarely left her room these days and he would often hear her sobbing late into the night. Sometimes he wondered whether he should go in and comfort her, and once had almost done so when she sounded well-nigh hysterical, but then Mrs Petty had come bustling along.

'I'll see to yer poor mam. I'll give her one of my potions,' she'd said, indicating the brown bottle in her hand. Mrs P was the nearest thing to a witch anyone could imagine.

Callum had left her to it, and while he was thankful to be free of the responsibility, not being entirely sure what he would have done if he'd gone in, he'd also felt a nudge of envy. It might be quite nice to be needed by your mother, for her to want you to sit beside her and know exactly what to do to help. But should Kate ever feel the need to have him by her, she had only to ask. So far, there'd been silence. Even the crying seemed to have stopped now.

Sometimes he offered to take in her breakfast or dinner on a tray. Generally she was lying in bed, oblivious of the fact that he was there. Until this morning when he'd discovered her sitting in a chair, staring blankly out of the window. He wondered if she'd been there all night.

'I've brought you breakfast,' he said, as he always did.

Rarely did she even respond, except on her better mornings. Sometimes she would smile a little, thank him or say that he was a good boy. Callum loved to see her smile. He ached to make her happy again.

This morning Kate startled him by saying: 'Would we have been happier, do you think Callum, if we'd stayed in Poor House Lane? Millie did, and she survived, along with most of her brood.'

'I don't know, Mam.' He liked calling her that, and did it more and more. It was much less formal, more personal somehow than mother.

He was rewarded with another of her rare smiles, as if she liked it too, but there was still that faint crease between her brow as if she sought the answer to a puzzle. 'Did I do the right thing? That's what I keep asking myself. It was for you, I did it for you. I was so afraid you might catch something dreadful and die. I wanted the best for you. Do you hate me for that? I didn't mean to give you away and nor did I, not entirely. I wouldn't have agreed to the adoption if they hadn't let me stay on as your nursemaid. Well, that was my official title, but you and me knew different. Wasn't I always your mammy?'

'Aye, Mam, you were.' Flora still called her Mammy, but Callum didn't. He was nearly a man after all.

'But then you vanished and my world fell apart. I went back to Poor House Lane. Did you know that?'

He was surprised. He hadn't known that.

'Now I've lost him. I've lost my Eliot. Why do I always lose those I love best? Is it a punishment for wanting too much from life, for being greedy?' Her eyes filled with tears and Callum hurried forward to give her an awkward pat on her shoulder.

'Of course it isn't a punishment. Anyroad, who from?'

'From the gods. They get jealous if we mere mortals are too happy, so they do.'

Callum made a scornful sound deep in his throat. 'You've been listening too much to Mrs P and her weird notions. The old witch is poisoning yer mind. You were poor, near starving, stands to reason you'd want to better yerself. Who wouldn't? And from all accounts, tha's med a grand job of the business. All the men say so.'

'Do they?' She perked up a little at that, but then seemed to collapse in upon herself. 'But how can I carry on? How can I go on without him?' And she put her face in her hands and sobbed.

Life had been difficult enough before, but now the situation was a thousand times worse. And that accident was all far too convenient. Why had they never found the car that had hit him? Why was it going so fast, and why didn't it stop? It all sounded a bit fishy to Callum.

What was worse, as a result of Eliot Tyson's death, Lucy now owned nearly a half-share in the company. She was forever flouncing about the house as if she owned that too. And while his mother continued to lock herself in her room, she might as well.

Kate was filled with a terrible restlessness. If she sat on her window seat for five minutes, she must then get up and go and sit on her chair by the fire, or lie on her bed for a while. She would pick up a book and try to read, or glance at the newspaper, but the things that were happening in the world – riots in Liverpool in response to a police strike, with hundreds arrested and talk of a rail strike soon – seemed unreal. Kate was too tired to care. She wasn't going anywhere, so what did it matter if the trains weren't running?

Thoughts tumbled over themselves in her head. She kept asking herself why it had happened, replaying that day in her mind like a stuck gramophone record.

Had Eliot been thinking of her and the baby, was that why he was knocked down? Because he hadn't been paying proper attention to what he was doing.

What a dreadful thought. In that case it would all be her fault. The more rational part of her mind told her this was nonsense, but then the questions and the need to apportion blame would start up all over again.

'It's my fault that I lost the baby,' she told Flora, as the little girl sat stroking her hand. Flora was appalled.

'Don't say such a terrible thing, Mammy. It is not your fault at all. You were grieving for Daddy. You were sick. Aunt Vera said you might have died.' Her lovely chestnut eyes filled with tears. 'What would I have done then, if you had died?'

'Aw, cherub, I'd never leave you, I swear it.' And she grasped Flora to her breast while the pair of them sobbed out their grief. Then Kate pulled out her hanky and scolded herself for giving in to her emotions, trying to smile, for the sake of her little girl. But scarcely were the words out of Kate's mouth before the tears were flowing again. They just wouldn't stop.

And when she wasn't crying, she felt sick, nauseous. Sometimes she would shake with cold, even as sweat slicked her skin as she constantly relived those dreadful moments when Constable Brown brought her the news.

Worse than that, in her mind's eye she saw the car, mysterious and black, driving very fast. She saw Eliot's startled expression transfixed and blinded by the sun glinting on its windscreen, eyes wide with terror. She heard the screech of brakes, the impact of a heavy body on steel, the sound of glass breaking. It seemed so real in her mind, almost as if she'd personally witnessed the event.

If she could but focus her mind on the sequence of events, on how the accident could have happened, yet it seemed impossible. One minute it was numb, the next racing, not a coherent thought in it, only a tumult of questions going round and round in her head.

Who had been driving that car? Why had the driver not bothered to stop? Who would be so cruel, so uncaring? Or was it simply fear that had made them drive on?

Most terrifying of all, she needed to know if Eliot had died instantly, or if he'd lain in the road dying slowly as he waited for help? Oh, it was all too awful to contemplate, too dreadful and confusing.

If only she had the answers to these questions, she might then be able to accept that he was dead, that he wasn't ever coming back to her. And yet a part of her still expected the door to open and Eliot to come breezing in, sweep her up into his arms and tell her how much he loved her.

Sometimes one of the aunts would creep in. Vera with hot lemon, as if she had 'flu or a sore throat, Cissie with a chocolate drop or mint humbug, as if she were a dog needing a treat. They brought her cups of tea she couldn't drink, meals she couldn't eat, their eyes full of pity.

The nights were the worst, long and silent and endless, her body aching from exhaustion as she sat and rocked herself in anguish in the chair, Eliot's photograph clutched to her chest. Sometimes she would walk quietly down the stairs and out into the starry night, slip through the stillness of the garden, as she was doing now, the heady scent of night-stocks filling her nostrils.

The will had given Lucy everything she'd ever wanted, and Kate felt as if she had nothing. She'd lost her child, most of the business that she'd worked so hard to build up, and even her beloved Eliot. How was she ever going to live without him? One short step and she'd back where she started, in Poor House Lane.

Oh, but she still had Callum, and Flora, she reminded herself. And didn't her children mean the world to her?

She sat in the summer house, not crying now but with a small smile on her face, remembering, finding some solace and peace at last in blissful memories. And she kept on counting her blessings, the ones she had found through Eliot's great love for her, and those she found in her children, and in her work. She sat on, oblivious to the cool night, thinking. When dawn crept over the horizon, only then did she go back inside and called her children to her side.

'What would Daddy say if he could see us now?' she asked, as the pair of them stood together, watching her with an anxious expression on their lovely young faces, Flora clinging to her older brother as if for support. 'Sure and he'd be ashamed of me, so he would. I remember him once telling me that I must never be defeated, or give in to self-pity if the worst happened and he didn't ever come back from the war. "Grieve for a little, if you must, but then you must get on with life," he'd say. "Nobody guarantees that we'll all have our three score years and ten, now do they?" And that's what we're going to have to do m'cushla. Like it or no, I'm going to pull myself together for the umpteenth time, and find some way to go on without him. Will you help me?'

'Oh, yes Mammy, we will,' cried Flora running into her mother's arms.

'You can always count on me,' said Callum.

Kate smiled into her son's eyes. 'And didn't I know that all along?'